# WHAT OTHE

"If you have the inspiration, this book can be your education."
> —**Bernie S. Siegel, M.D.**, author of *Love, Medicine & Miracles*
> and *Peace, Love and Healing*

"This book is the finest gift you could give to anyone you love and want to see happy. With her brilliant insights, this wise author runs deep and accurate . . . and releases us from most of the terrible ignorance that can literally kill any one of us."
> —**Arnold "Nick" Carter**, Vice President, Nightingale-Conant

"If you want to jump-start your life, personally and professionally, read this book now! Do not let another day slip past without incorporating these life-changing insights into your daily experience."
> —**Glenna Salsbury**, CSP, CPAE,
> author of *The Art of The Fresh Start*,
> President, 1997–98, National Speakers Association

"Cathy Lauro is an inspired individual who is passionate about sharing her life-changing experiences with others who are committed to making a difference in their lives. This book is a practical guide with fundamental self-improvement philosophies that can help 'ordinary people accomplish extraordinary things.'"
> —**Herren Hickingbotham**, President, TCBY Enterprises, Inc.

"This book condenses three decades of mind/body research into user-friendly exercises sure to induce personal growth and improved health."
> —**Stephanie Simonton, Ph.D.**, Director, Behavioral Medicine,
> University of Arkansas Medical Sciences, co-author of
> *Getting Well Again*

"When you are fed up with being the way you are, this book can help you become the person you have always wanted to be."
> —**Winthrop P. Rockefeller**, Lieutenant Governor of Arkansas

"I am delighted to know Cathy Lauro. Her passion for her message, which comes through so strongly and so beautifully in her writing, is even more evident when one experiences her in person. She truly does love her work, and this exceptional book is an expression of that love. The mark of a true healer, in my mind, is the ability to be authentically with another individual so fully and completely that one can truly understand the other's experience of pain. Cathy Lauro is a healer. She's been there and back, and hers is an experienced voice of strength and hope and guidance. Read this book well. There is wisdom here."
> — **Stephen A. Hathcock, M.D.**, Director, The Center For Integrative Medicine

"This book is filled with techniques that really work. Cathy has made this information easy to digest with her insight, humor, and heart. If you want to gain greater control over your future, you need to read *The Inside Advantage*."
> — **Lee E. Robert**, President, Cavett Robert Communications

"The beauty of this book is that it gives the reader a tool that has been proven scientifically to bring about a healthy physiological and emotional state."
> — **Linda Hodges, Ed.D., R.N.**, Dean, College of Nursing, University of Arkansas Medical Sciences, co-author of *The Older Adult*

"I highly recommend this practical guide for anyone wanting to be happier, healthier, and more successful in their personal and professional lives."
> — **Patti Upton**, President and CEO, Aromatique, Inc.

"Step by step, and exercise by exercise, Cathy Lauro's *The Inside Advantage* helps all of us achieve more in life. This 'must read' book will have a positive effect on our world."
> — **Joe Sabah**, author of *How to Get on Radio Talk Shows All Across America Without Leaving Your Home or Office*

"Cathy's insight on what any professional needs today is evident in this book. Many of her statements and stories really hit home and motivated me to strive to a new level professionally. You do not want to miss reading this book to chart a new course for your life. It's never too late to learn and grow."
> —**Kathleen McComber**, Chair, National Board of Directors, Society for Human Resource Management (SHRM)

"If you want to get out of a rut, this book is for you! This work is the most eye-opening, engaging self-fulfillment book I have ever read—gently done and powerfully moving. Cathy's style of writing, her anecdotes, true life experiences, and gentle challenges guide you toward gaining your 'Inside Advantage.'"
> —**L. Paul Ouellette,** CSP
> CEO, Ouellette and Associates,
> author, *I/S Internal Consulting*

"We all get caught up in the fast-paced and detail-filled aspects of our lives. Sometimes we need to step back and focus on what is really important. This book can truly help you achieve that much-needed, different perspective."
> —**Diahann W. Lassus**, President, 1998–99, National Association of Women Business Owners

"With this exceptional book, Cathy educates your mind, touches your heart, and lights up your life."
> —**Jennings Osborne**, Arkansas Research Medical Testing, philanthropist who lights up Walt Disney World during Christmas

"Cathy Lauro is an extraordinary person with so much to give to others. Her book is extraordinary and will give hope, love, thought and power to many who have need of it."
> —**Willie Oates**, fund raiser and "Mad Hatter"

"Great insights and practical ideas and strategies for living a successful life."
> —**Patricia Fripp,** CSP, CPAE, author of *Get What You Want* Past President, National Speakers Association

# The
# INSIDE
# ADVANTAGE

*To Melinda,*
*You are extraordinary!*
*Coach Lauro*

# The INSIDE ADVANTAGE

## How ordinary people can accomplish EXTRAORDINARY things

CATHY W. LAURO

*Select Press*

*Corte Madera, CA*

Select Press
P.O. Box 37
Corte Madera, CA 94976-0037
(415) 435-4461

The Inside Advantage: How ordinary people
accomplish extraordinary things / Cathy W. Lauro

ISBN  1-890777-08-0

Published in the United States of America
Printed in Canada

# Contents

# Foreword

Why did you pick up this book? You're probably intrigued with the journey from ordinary to extraordinary. What could you accomplish if you believed you could? You may want to change the way you think and feel, emotionally or physically. Your life may not be exactly where you want it to be, and you don't know what to do about it. Maybe your life is just where you thought you wanted it to be; you've reached your level of defined success, but you're not as happy as you had hoped.

The dreams we have for our futures often get sidelined by the so-called realities of life. These "realities" include family obligations, job responsibilities, unforeseen events, and plain exhaustion. Yet you see others who are taking control of their lives as they excel in every area. How do they do it? How can you do the same thing? Is it luck, education, street smart savvy, or something else? Forget luck; mostly luck happens in movies. Education doesn't guarantee you anything other than a diploma. Street smart savvy can help you succeed only to a limited degree.

I know from personal experience that only through peace of mind can you experience health, happiness, and success. But, how do you find peace of mind? What will take you from where you are and put you where you want to be? The answer is simple: learn to change how you think about yourself and the world around you. Sounds simple, doesn't it? Then why isn't everyone experiencing life joyfully and successfully?

Many people don't know where to begin; they're lost from the start. Others have a difficult time trying to find their way, and wind up taking unexpected turns and detours. It's much easier when you have a map.

Cathy W. Lauro provides the map you need to change your life. You're going to get a full set of instructions to show you how to find your way. On this journey you will discover many things about yourself and what's really important to you. You'll learn how your mind works, how to use visualization and imagery, ways to reduce stress and stay well, and much more.

Everything you will learn focuses on one ultimate goal: accomplishing extraordinary things. If your dream is to improve your relationships, your career, your entire life, then turn the page and start now. You have the map; you just need to begin the journey.

> — Pam Lontos
> Lontos Sales & Motivation, Inc.
> Orlando, Florida

# Special Thanks

I want to express my heartfelt gratitude to all the people who have touched my life in special ways and who have helped me accomplish extraordinary things.

*My special thanks to:*

Michael, my wonderful husband, and the most extraordinary man I have ever met, for his constant support, encouragement, and love.

Mike Lauro, Jr., my incredibly amazing son, my life's most precious gift, who has taught me so much about life, love, joy, and success.

Catherine Memory Ellis, an exceptional woman, who loved me unconditionally and showed me how to live deeply.

Iris and John E. Wenzel, my dear parents, who have always done their best, from whom I have learned valuable lessons.

Dezlie Wenzel Fried, my talented sister, a special spirit with a heart of gold, who has helped me see things beyond what is visible. Her voice, music, and songs touch listeners' souls. (She created the music on *The Inside Advantage*® audio programs.)

Johnny "Butch" Wenzel, my kind-hearted brother, who inspired me to adopt the philosophy, "Work smart, play hard, live well."

The rest of my family and friends for the special parts they play in my life. I love and cherish all of you!

My teachers, mentors, and colleagues who taught me well and encouraged me to believe in myself.

My students for teaching me more of what I needed to know.

All of the individuals who have shared with me what was on their minds and in their hearts. Thank you for letting me help you.

* * * * * * *

I also wish to give sincere thanks to all of those who provided invaluable assistance in this extraordinary endeavor, especially:

| | |
|---|---|
| Michael V. Lauro | John E. Wenzel |
| Mike Lauro, Jr. | Pam Lontos |
| Allan L. Ward, Ph.D. | Kay Danielson |
| Judith C. Lowrey | Mary Ann Campbell |
| Linda Hodges, Ed.D., R.N. | Louis M. Miller, Ph.D. |
| Rick Crandall, Ph.D. | Carolynn Crandall |

# Introduction

*Nothing will come of nothing. Dare mighty things.*
—WILLIAM SHAKESPEARE

## What Is The Inside Advantage?

The Inside Advantage is:

- a valuable tool to help you change the way you experience life, believing in yourself and your abilities
- a practical guide for understanding the mind—how it works and how you can use it more effectively to accomplish extraordinary things
- the strengths you gain when you tap into your inner resources—your mind and heart—and get them to work together in agreement
- an attitude—living deeply, joyfully, and successfully

I magine! Ordinary people accomplishing extraordinary things! What do we think of when we apply the descriptive word *ordinary* to people? Typically, we mean common, traditional, normal, average, regular people like you and me. What do we mean by *extraordinary*? We might think of words such as uncommon, unusual, incredible, exceptional, and amazing. Do most people think of themselves as extraordinary? Unfortunately not, but the truth is that we indeed are remarkable and we can accomplish extraordinary things. If we begin to think of ourselves as incredible and exceptional, we can become what we think.

The intention of this book is to help you make positive changes to enrich your life. The great astronomer Galileo said, "You cannot teach a man anything. You can only help him to find it within himself." Did you know that the word *educate* is derived from the Latin word meaning "to bring out from within"? This is the idea behind the name *The Inside Advantage*. It refers to the attitude we have when we live deeply. It also refers to the benefits we gain by tapping into our inner resources. We can live more joyfully and successfully by getting our hearts and minds to work together in agreement. To do that we need to take advantage of our finest gift and most valuable tool—the mind.

Our minds are always working—either for or against us—as our greatest allies or our worst enemies. It's up to each of us to use all the resources within us to accomplish anything we set our minds to do; and to do that is nothing short of extraordinary!

> *To go from being ordinary to extraordinary,*
> *a transformation or change must occur*
> *in our thoughts (how we think),*
> *in our beliefs (what we feel in our hearts),*
> *and in our actions (what we do).*

When we put our minds to work for us, we not only alter the way we think, but we also change our physical sensations, emotional feelings, and behaviors.

*The Inside Advantage* is a valuable learning tool designed to help ordinary people believe in themselves and their abilities to accomplish extraordinary things. It also serves as a practical guide for understanding the mind, how it works, and how we can use it more effectively.

What do we use our minds for? Everything! Therefore the possibilities are limitless. Consider using your mind to develop the astounding untapped potential within you. Challenge yourself; you will be surprised by what you can achieve.

Take a moment and ask yourself, "If I could change my life in a positive way, if I could do something extraordinary, what would I do?"

Would you want to:

- change the way you feel about yourself?
- change the way you feel about others?
- increase self-esteem and confidence?
- reduce stress and anxiety?
- eliminate fears?
- release negative emotions?
- forgive yourself and others?
- enhance wellness?
- improve job performance?
- increase sales?
- perform well on tests?
- eliminate negative habits?
- improve sports performance?
- gain peace of mind?

Know that accomplishing even one thing on this list *is* extraordinary.

Think how much better your life would be if you changed just one thing. What if you actually liked the person you are? What if you could forgive your parents or people who have hurt you? Would your life be better if you could let go of anger, guilt, regret, and even worry about the future? Do you want to be happier, healthier, and more successful at living?

If you could do any of these things, what would that mean to you? How would you feel? What would the ripple effects be? If one thing changed, what else would change? Would you feel more in control of your life? Absolutely!

> ***When you change your mind,***
> ***it can change everything!***

Do you hate going to the dentist? What if you were rushed to the emergency room in terrible pain? Do you have a plan of action to put your mind to work for you in these types of situations? Have you even thought about it? Most people haven't. Changing anything that is of significance to you (from escaping in your mind as the nurse sticks you with a needle to building self-esteem and confidence) is extraordinary!

If you decide that it's time to take more control over your life, if you want to accomplish extraordinary things, then you are ready to gain *The Inside Advantage.*

I have spent most of my life researching, practicing, and teaching others how to use their minds more effectively. I am thrilled to be able to share with you what I have learned so that you can create your life more the way you want it to be. I hope that you will open your mind as you read, and allow yourself to think in new and different ways. Take what you need and put it to use for your benefit. You will find many practical exercises that will help clarify ideas and techniques. I've also included some of my personal stories—perhaps you will relate to them and be able to use my "journeys" to speed your progress towards extraordinary. At times when you find that you are listening to the words between the lines, I sincerely hope to touch your heart.

T.S. Eliot, in *Little Guilding,* speaks of forever exploring who we are. When we come to the end of our exploration, we arrive where we first started, knowing the place for the very first time. You are about to embark on an incredible journey that will take you to places you may never have imagined!

When you gain *The Inside Advantage,* you will have the treasure map to help you find your way from ordinary to extraordinary. Bon voyage!

---

Please do not be offended by gender-specific quotations. It was the way they were originally written. Any gender-specific references are used for simplification and ease of reading.

# 1

# Let's Get Started!

*The real voyage of discovery consists not in
seeking new landscapes, but in having new eyes.*
—Marcel Proust

C hanging the way we see things means changing our perceptions of ourselves and the world around us. It means gaining
*The Inside Advantage* and, to do that, we start where our most
important journey begins—in the mind.

Most of us use only a fraction of our minds' potential—
about ten percent. Why is this? The best answer is that we are
simply unaware of what our minds can do for us. Peter Kline,
author of *The Everyday Genius*, tells us "Somewhere inside of you
is your own sort of genius—waiting and wondering when you'll
care enough to call it forth."

The mind is like a powerful computer that will do just about
anything we want it to—if it receives the appropriate instructions.
At any given time, it is doing its best, relying on instructions from
the past that have already been written. Whether we realize it or
not, we are constantly programming our internal computer through

our interpretations of incoming information. Over time, we create habits—patterns of thinking, feeling, and behaving. They are like mini-programs in our computer-like brains; they define how we view ourselves and all that surrounds us. If the habits we have created are working for us, that's great! Many of them already are, but if there are some that are not, we can change or reprogram them. Marcus Aurelius, an early Roman emperor said, "The universe is transformation. Our life is what our thoughts make it."

## Immediate Needs

Sometimes we need to put our minds to work in the *present* moment to temporarily change our experience of the current situation. An example of this process would be when you are in the dentist's office to have some work done. The dentist is coming toward you with a needle that seems a foot long. You hear, "This is going to hurt." All you want to do is jump out of the chair! At this point, you can either put your mind to work for you or let it work against you. If you sit there and focus on how much it's going to hurt, guess what? It's really going to hurt! When a dentist once told me that, I immediately said, "No, it's not." Then I began to use some of the techniques I will share with you.

Taking control is the key. It's easy once you learn how. You can train your mind to immediately go to work *for* you instead of *against* you whenever you need it. You will automatically take more control over your thoughts, mental images, feelings and, ultimately, your behavior.

## Long-Term Changes

We can also use our minds to make changes that will be long lasting, perhaps changes that will drastically alter our lives. These kinds of changes could include: taking control of our bad habits, becoming more of the kind of person we want to be, feeling the way we want to feel, increasing our personal and professional effectiveness, creating for ourselves lives in which we can experience more success, joy, and peace of mind—living more fully. Is this possible? Of course it is!

# Locus of Control

*Locus of personal control* is the term psychologists use when referring to your feelings of control over your life. Some people learn that they are the masters of their own fates and therefore bear the responsibility for what happens to them. We can refer to these individuals as "inner-directed." Inner-directed people operate under the assumption that they have a great deal of control over their lives; they see the control as coming from inside themselves. These are people who strongly believe that what they do can make a difference in their experiences of life. They work hard to create positive change for themselves. They make lemonade when life hands them lemons.

"Outer-directed" individuals believe that outside forces (the environment, other people, organizations, circumstances, and so forth) are basically responsible for how their lives turn out. They feel that they have little, if any, influence over what happens to them. They blame everything and everyone, except themselves, for their problems. They complain about the lemons, wishing and waiting passively for oranges instead.

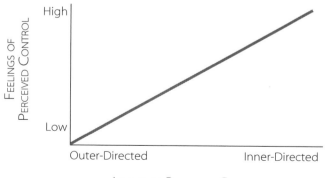

LOCUS OF PERSONAL CONTROL

As you can see in the chart on the previous page, the more outer-directed you are, the *less control* you feel you have. The more inner-directed you are, the *more control* you feel you have.

## Turn Weaknesses into Strengths

From our weaknesses, we can find strength. William Arthur Ward, educator and author, said, "Adversity causes some men to break, others to break records." While we all have weaknesses, handicaps, and limitations, it is what we do in response to them that matters.

After becoming totally deaf, Beethoven composed great symphonies. Norman Vincent Peale, the author of many self-improvement books, including *The Power of Positive Thinking*, was extremely self-conscious as a young man. He said, "I probably had the biggest inferiority complex that ever existed." He achieved greatness because of his desire to overcome those feelings. Helen Keller, blind and deaf from birth, said, "I thank God for my handicaps!"

Our weaknesses are opportunities for us to learn important lessons that help us grow as human beings. After a college class one day, I told my professor about an interesting personal experience. He asked me to share that story with our class the next week. I was frightened at the very thought of having to speak in public. "No way! I can't get up in front of fifty people and talk. You don't understand; I just can't." I left his office and felt awful; I was walking away from a challenge (an opportunity to grow) and I did not feel good about myself for doing that. I wanted to be able to share my experience with the group, but my level of self-esteem, self-consciousness, and fear of rejection held me back.

As I walked across campus, I had a long internal dialog with myself in which I made an important decision. I did not like the idea of running away from things. I had done it all my life; it was time to stop. I decided to go far beyond my comfort zone and use this opportunity to become more of the kind of person I always wanted to be. I turned around, went back up to his office, and said, "I'll do it." You can imagine how terrified I felt at the realization of what I had just done.

For the next seven days I practiced my presentation at home. The following week I went to class. It was time! The professor introduced me and I slowly walked to the front of the classroom. I was very nervous, but a part of me felt excited. I was actually doing something that was very difficult for me. I was facing fear rather than running from it, and that felt good. I stood rigidly with my arms straight down by my sides. My mouth was dry; butterflies were fluttering in my stomach, and I could feel my heart pounding. I could barely get the words out, but I told my story. Twenty minutes later I finished. I was so happy that it was over! I had done it!

After I stopped speaking, something amazing and unexpected happened—the whole class clapped! The room was small, and fifty people were clapping. I will never forget that sound and how exhilarated I felt! I was so proud of myself. No one except the professor knew how difficult it had been for me. I saw him smile; I think he understood my personal triumph. I learned how to be courageous.

Don't let your limitations and weaknesses discourage you. Face them, learn from them, and use them to find strength in yourself. Eddie Rickenbacker, the famous World War I pilot, said, "Courage is doing what you're afraid to do. There can be no courage unless you're scared."

 ***Our weaknesses are opportunities to learn important lessons.***

**2**

# *What If Your Life Is Not the Way You Want It to Be?*

*To move the world we must first move ourselves.*

—SOCRATES

Most of us are struggling just to get through the day, trying to cope with life the best way we know how. Performing stressful or boring jobs, rushing here and there, buying food and clothes, paying bills, taking care of others, doing what we have to do just to survive.

Sometimes we may wonder, "Why is my life so different from the way I want it to be? Why am I not the way I want to be? How did I get here? Why am I feeling stressed and unhappy?" These are typical questions many of us ask at one time or another. We need to realize that progress comes from discontent with the way things are. If we are unhappy with ourselves or our situations, that's when we become motivated to do something about it.

# But . . . I Don't Know
# What I Want to Do

I worked in training and human resource management for ten years. All the while, in the back of my mind, I could still hear the voice of my favorite professor, Allan Ward, Ph.D. He once said, "I love my job so much I would do it even if I didn't get paid for it." I always wanted that for myself. "Why not me?" I asked.

I started out after graduate school working in jobs that, at the time, seemed practical; they were ways to make money. After a short time I realized that I didn't have my heart in my work, but I kept on doing it. It was what I thought I should be doing. "I can't quit now; what else would I do?" So I continued working in jobs where my head told me I was supposed to be. My heart always said something else: "What are you doing here? This is not where you belong." The problem was that I didn't know what I really wanted to do with my life or where I belonged. However, I knew what I did *not* want to do and where I did *not* want to be.

Do not underestimate the value of learning this kind of information about yourself. This will give you some direction, leading you away from places and situations that don't suit you. Listen to your heart, your intuition, your gut feelings; it's a way to hear what is best for you.

# When Will I Move Forward?

Most people go through life wanting things to be different and hoping luck will eventually change things. Have you noticed that some people constantly complain about the way things are? They say they want to change and that they want their circumstances to be different, but they never do anything about it. They expect certain things to occur, but their actions have little or nothing to do with making them happen. They may feel miserably unhappy, but at least it's a familiar situation; and, in an odd sort of way, they feel secure in their misery. Maybe they fear the idea of change. It may be too uncomfortable to even think about, let alone do something that might make a difference. They may come to a point in their lives when they realize that staying the same makes them more afraid than changing. Then they will be ready to take the first steps to move forward.

For much of my young life, I was unhappy with who I was. I was painfully shy and afraid I would always be that way. Eventually, the fear of staying the same became more frightening than the fear of actually making changes. That's when I began to take action to make my life better.

 ***We are ready to move forward when staying the same is more fearful than change.***

## The Good News

We often look to others to somehow make it all better. Sometimes we try to get what we need from relationships, or perhaps we turn to food, alcohol, or drugs to make us feel whole and to dull our pain. However, when we look outside of ourselves to fulfill our needs, we're looking in the wrong direction!

Here is an intriguing concept to think about for a moment: What if all you have ever needed—strength, courage, confidence, a best friend, acceptance, peace, love, and joy—everything to make your life better, was right there within your grasp all along? The good news is: All of that and more is already within you! You can think of these things as gifts that you are born with, things that have been misplaced and must be rediscovered. This is one of the most important and profound discoveries I have ever made for myself. If we could only believe this truth early in life, it would save us so much time and energy, so much pain and sorrow.

 *Everything I need is already within me.*

Say the above statement out loud right now and let your ears hear this—maybe for the first time. You may want to get a piece of paper and pencil now, and write down this statement. Then read it to yourself aloud and listen to its meaning.

Being open to this message means being open to the idea that your journey inward will lead you to discover your gifts and hidden treasures. Consider for a moment what understanding and believing this concept could mean to you. Would this help you feel better about yourself? Would you feel better equipped to cope with what life hands you? If this were true, would you be able to re-create your life the way you want it to be? Of course!

 ***Begin to believe in yourself.***

## What Is Needed for Change to Occur?

A *desire* to create change is often linked to *inspiration*. You may be inspired through an experience, something you read or hear, or perhaps a person you meet. It could be a combination of several things. Inspiration (usually from an outside source) and *motivation* (more of an inner drive) are also closely linked. You may be at a point in your life where you are tired of feeling "stuck," and you are ready to move on. You also need a *vision* of what you want to achieve and where you want to go. *Action* is taking specific steps in that direction, actually doing something about yourself or your situation. You must also develop a *belief* that you can do it, that you can accomplish something extraordinary. You must also have an *expectation* that the outcome will occur as you envision it.

We all daydream of the future, hoping it will be better. But, when we daydream, we don't really believe it will happen. It's like wishing, and all the while believing it's impossible.

We can create the future the way we envision it—*if* we take action and *if* we believe in our hearts that it can happen. We must make a commitment to ourselves to accomplish extraordinary things. Author Peter Drucker said, "Unless commitment is made, there are only promises and hopes . . . but no plans." Use your mind to develop your plans for the future.

For many people, developing beliefs is the most difficult part. When we read books or attend workshops, we often learn what we must do to make positive changes. However, if deep down we do not truly believe that we are capable of accomplishing a particular goal, we never will. Helping individuals bridge the gap between knowing what to do and actually doing it is the focus of my work. It is absolutely necessary that we develop a belief system that supports us in all that we want to accomplish. Fortunately, it's much easier than most people think!

## Aim for Excellence Rather than Perfection

Let me tell you a story to clarify what is needed to bring about change. Years ago when I was extremely shy and had very low self-esteem, it seemed that everyone except me was happy. Even when there were good things going on, and I should have been happy, I was miserable on the inside. I believed that I was worthless and was undeserving of anything good in my life. I desperately tried to do the right things. I felt that I could only be accepted and loved if I did everything perfectly. No matter what I did, or how hard I tried, it seemed as if it was never good enough. When the goal is perfection, you will always fall short. Later I learned to aim for excellence instead.

I did not want to continue to experience my life in such negative ways; I was tired of hurting emotionally. I wanted to be happy. I wanted to feel good about myself. Not only did I have a desire to change from the inside, I also became inspired and motivated to do whatever it would take to transform my life. I read self-help books and attended workshops to try to understand myself better.

I created a vision of what I wanted my life to be like, specifically how I wanted to think and feel, and how I wanted to act. Finally, I was beginning to do something about me. Once I learned how to change my beliefs about myself, I expected my life to change for the better. I knew it would, and it did. This can also happen for you.

*The journey starts with a strong*
*DESIRE to move forward.*

## The Secret of Success

An important message can be found in a story that I heard many years ago. A young boy asked his grandfather to teach him what he needed to know so that he could grow up to be successful. The wise old man agreed, then took the boy's hand and led him down to the nearby lake. They waded into the water together. The boy was puzzled, but he trusted his grandfather. Suddenly the man grabbed the boy by the back of the neck and pushed his head underwater. The boy struggled, frantically waving his arms and splashing in the water, thrashing his body back and forth, trying desperately to raise his head. Finally the old man released his hold. The boy shot up out of the lake, gasping for air. The child cried, "I don't understand! Why did you try to drown me?" "Son," said his grandfather, ". . . when you want something in life as much as you wanted to breathe just now, you'll have it."

If you want to accomplish something badly enough and it is within your control, you'll find a way to make it happen. Concentrate your energy on what you want to change. In the process, do your best to distinguish between those things that you can and cannot control. Trying to change someone else to make your life better is usually a waste of time and energy. Many of our problems stem from trying to get others to do what we want. We are truly powerless in changing others, so focus on YOU for a CHANGE!

*All we can control is ourselves—*
*what we think, how we feel,*
*and what we do.*

## Clearing the Mental Jungle

When we begin to think, feel, and act in new ways, the brain and nervous system create new neural pathways—like clearing a path through a jungle. At first there is no path, just trees and vegetation ahead. Even though it may be uncomfortable or difficult, we make our way through unknown territory, cutting and clearing away all of the barriers. Then we look back and know that the next time we pass this way it will be easier. The more we travel this path, once we clear it, the more worn it becomes. This makes traveling much easier.

Similarly, the pathways in our minds that are easiest for us to travel are the ones that are used frequently. The more often we think, feel, and behave in certain patterns, the more worn those paths become, and the easier it is for us to respond in those particular ways.

It is important to understand that just because we use certain paths does not mean they lead to places we want to go, or even to places that are good for us. Many times we go down the same old road just because it's familiar. At other times we do this because it's easier than taking a new road, and definitely less work than clearing a totally new path for ourselves. We may be afraid of unknown territory. We begin to worry. What if we changed? What if we find something on the new path that is worse than the path we are on? Fear keeps us from moving ahead, doesn't it?

If we want to make changes in the way we experience life, if the old ways are not working to our advantage, we must clear new pathways through our mental jungles. We need to go to work changing our thoughts, mental images, and feelings. We have to do things differently from the way we have done them in the past.

## Two Different Earrings

If you should ever see me in person, you will find me wearing two different earrings, one on each earlobe. I do this because to me, it represents being open to change. Just because we have done things in certain ways in the past does not mean we have to continue doing them. We are always free to choose not only our thoughts and mental images, but also our behaviors. We need to realize that at any given moment we are free to create our futures more the way we want them to be.

Wearing unmatched earrings may sound like an easy thing to do; it wasn't for me. Being a nonconformist was not how I had defined myself. After all, I had been very self-conscious; I tried to be perfect. In the past, I certainly would not have wanted to draw attention to myself because then I would be more open to criticism and rejection. Wearing unmatched earrings is not what most people expect to see. What would people think? That was one of my biggest problems—caring so much about what others thought of me. Over time, I have come to believe deep down that it really does not matter what other people's opinions of me are, as long as I believe in myself. I know that I am always doing my best under the circumstances. I have learned not to ask more than that of myself.

By using the same techniques you will find in this book, I have been able to develop strong beliefs in my heart: feelings of self-acceptance, self-love, and high, positive self-esteem. Trust that you, too, can clear new pathways. You can feel good about yourself in spite of what others may think, say, or do. Don't let the ways of the past keep you from experimenting with whom you might want to become.

 *The future does not have to be a continuation of the past.*

The past, with all of its experiences (good and bad), is important because that is what has brought you to the point where you are right now. However, what is even more important than where you have been, is how you imagine your future. You have a choice between living in the past or focusing your energy on where you want to go.

## What Is an "Ordinary" Person to Do?

To live, you have to interact successfully with the world around you. To live fully, you need to create joy in your life every day, no matter what else is going on. You also need to know who you are inside. You must learn to believe in yourself and your capabilities. You have vast inner resources to draw upon to correct what you think and feel is wrong in your life. Trusting in yourself gives you the strength to accomplish extraordinary things!

What do you need to do to live more joyfully and success-fully? *Read this book* for starters; become inspired and motivated. Take time out to *do the exercises.* When you are ready, put your mind to work (take action) by following the steps in Chapter 17. *Apply the techniques* to reach your own personal and professional goals.

It sounds simple and easy, doesn't it? It really is. How do I know? It has worked wonderfully for me personally, and I have seen it work for so many individuals who truly wanted to make positive changes for themselves. I remember one woman who was in an unhappy marriage with a husband who had dominated her for over forty years. She wanted that to change. She told me, "I'm going to start taking control over my life. I want my sixties to be my best years." It's never too late to create positive lifelong changes. And she did!

### Take Responsibility

Accomplishing extraordinary things starts with taking responsibility for creating our futures. We need to become drivers instead of passengers. We usually cannot sit back and wait for positive changes to occur; we have to make them happen. We are in trouble if we expect life just to hand us everything we want. No one is going to come along, do it all for us, and give us everything we need. Ultimately, we must take responsibility to do it on our own.

We also need to remember that we should never let circum-stances dictate our lives. We do not have to be victims of what happens to us, at least not for long. If we continually feel victim-ized by life, perhaps it's because we think we have no other choice. We may not believe that spending time and energy trying to change things would actually make a difference.

Negative beliefs are also an excuse. If we let circumstances control our lives, then it would not be our fault if things didn't work out. Many people don't want to take responsibility for their own lives; it's easier to blame others for their unhappiness. When I was first married, I expected my husband to make me happy. I assigned him that job. Was that his responsibility? No! No one can do it for you. But anyone can accomplish extraordinary things by taking responsibility for creating success, peace, joy, and love in their own lives.

*Your life is what you make it;*
*what you make it is up to you.*

### Become Aware

One of the first steps in accomplishing extraordinary things is to become aware of the processes that go on inside our heads. To create a change in our behavior and our feelings, we must first become observers to the thought processes behind them. When we become aware of the patterns we have established out of habit, then we can begin to make the necessary adjustments. This journey inward is an exciting trip, a wonderful adventure. Be open to what you might discover within yourself.

*Your journey inward will lead*
*you to discover your gifts*
*and hidden treasures.*

### Take Control and Make It Happen

First, take responsibility for creating changes in your life and become aware of the processes involved, then take control and make it happen for yourself. Believe that you can do anything you set your mind to, as long as it's in your control. However, knowing what you want, and wishing for it will not be enough; you must take action.

Try thinking of life as a delicious buffet. At a buffet, what do you have to do? You must get up and get what you want. No one is going to bring food to you. If you sit and wait, you will miss out on a lot. You'll stay hungry. I challenge you to get up and get going! Take control. Experience life the way it was meant to be lived. Become all that you can be. Help yourself to life's buffet!

# 3

# *The Journey Within*

*Know thyself.*

—SOCRATES

**H** appiness is another name for inner joy. It comes from a state of being, rather than doing or having. Why aren't more of us feeling happy and content? The reason is that we tend to keep ourselves trapped on the surfaces of our lives; all we see is the tip of the iceberg. The problem many of us have is that we lack an understanding of our inner selves and the power of our minds to create our own moments of joy.

As we go through life, we rarely know what lies buried within our minds and hearts. Before we can begin to believe that everything we need is already within us, we must look below the surface. There may be some apprehension whenever we look into any unfamiliar place, especially within ourselves. We might not like what we find. However, to change or get rid of something negative, you at least have to know what it is. Trust that you will also find hidden treasures and special gifts.

This chapter is designed to help you with the process of looking inward. Once you face yourself and who you really are, you can begin to change all that limits you and keeps you from living life to the fullest. You can learn to live more deeply.

## Do You Know What Really Matters?

One of the most meaningful things that you can do for yourself is to stop and think about what really matters. Regardless of what kinds of changes you want to make, it is crucial to know what you truly value. When you know what is most important to you, you can live your life more authentically. You make better decisions because you have measured your options against your priorities. Your thoughts, feelings, and actions are in harmony; all parts of your life fit together better.

Let's begin to look inside.

EXERCISE: **Only One Year Left.** Take a few moments to write down on a sheet of paper, "If I only had one year to live, I would . . . ." Brainstorm and list all ideas that come to you. You can do this quickly or take as long as you like.

There is no reason that this exercise should be depressing; it can be very helpful and even fun to think about. This exercise really gives you a good overall perspective of the kinds of things that are important for you to accomplish and to enjoy. When you seem to have all the time in the world, if you are like most people, you tend to postpone some things that really are important.

As you put down on paper a mix of the ideas in your head and the feelings in your heart, you are able to take a closer look at where you need to be spending your time and energy now. In essence, what are your priorities?

You may want to do many things. All of them seem important, but some are more important than others. I don't want to have regrets about things I wanted to do and couldn't find the time. Do you?

One of the things on my list was to let all the people I truly cared about know how much they meant to me—relatives, friends, neighbors, etc. I sent handwritten notes to all of them. These were messages from the heart. Some simply said, "Thank you for being a special part of my life." Make plans to do the things on your list. There is no time like the present to get started.

# Values

To be successful in our lives, we need to know what our values are. When we know what we define as worthwhile, we can determine how to function at our best. When our thought and behavior patterns are congruent, if they match our basic values, then all is well. If they do not match, we experience stress, unhappiness, and a feeling that we are not doing what we seems to be right. *Cognitive dissonance* is a term psychologists use to describe the feeling we get when our behaviors differ considerably from our inherent values. We tend to be strongly motivated to reduce this difference. We do this by either changing our values (how we think and what we believe), or our behaviors.

 *To live fully, it is essential to think and act according to our core values.*

**What Are Your Most Important Priorities?**

All of the items on the following list are important; however, some will be more important to you than others. Please take a few moments and quickly read through these items, checking the ten values that you feel are most important to you. Don't think; just feel. Let your answers come from within; let your heart speak to you. Be completely honest with yourself. After you have done this, prioritize them by writing the numbers 1–10 next to the ones you have marked (1 = *most important*, 2 = *next most important*, and so on). There are no right or wrong answers. Your experiences and your interpretations of those experiences will determine your priorities. These may change over time.

EXERCISE: **What Is Most Important?**   Check your top 10 priorities, then rank them (1 = *most important,* etc.).

_____ accomplishments, challenges, overcoming obstacles
_____ an active, energetic lifestyle
_____ adventure and excitement
_____ close friends/companionship (a sense of belonging)
_____ competition
_____ creativity (ideas or activities)
_____ cultural activities
_____ effectiveness (doing the right things & doing them well)
_____ efficient use of time
_____ equality and justice
_____ family cohesiveness and nurturing
_____ financial security
_____ independence
_____ guiding, teaching, helping others
_____ good health
_____ interaction with others
_____ laughter
_____ leading others
_____ learning (personal and professional development)
_____ loyalty (to organizations, ideals, people)
_____ enjoyment of nature (the sea, mountains, forest, etc.)
_____ organized and clean surroundings
_____ peace of mind (inner peace)
_____ physical skill, challenge
_____ precision, accuracy, attention to detail
_____ being productive
_____ recognition and appreciation for your efforts
_____ respect from people whom you respect
_____ routine, stability
_____ self-respect
_____ sense of purpose and meaning
_____ sexual intimacy
_____ personal solitude, quiet time for relaxation
_____ spirituality, religion, belief in a higher power
_____ wisdom, maturity, insight
_____ other _____

You may want to write your top three priorities down on a small card, then read them a few times to reinforce them in your mind. Carry this card with you and refer to it often as a reminder of what is most important to you. You can even put the card in a place where you are sure to see it every day.

When you have choices to make on how to spend your time and energy, and perhaps your money, let these three priorities guide you in your decisions. They are at the heart of who you are. Knowing yourself and understanding what you value helps you become more successful at living fully. Remember, you can accomplish *anything* you want (if it is in your control), but not necessarily *everything* you want. There is not enough time to do it all. Knowing your priorities will help you to see more of the overall picture and what is right for you. When you think and act according to your core values, you automatically take more control over your life.

## Charting Your Course

Creating your future instead of just letting it happen to you requires asking yourself important questions. The Extraordinary Changes Questionnaire™ provided in the Appendix is designed to help facilitate the process of charting your course for change, one step at a time. It can be used over and over again, as many times as you need. It includes much of what you will find in this section.

Using the questionnaire will give you an opportunity to spend some time looking within yourself for answers as you reflect on your desires and motivation for change. Your answers can also be a source of valuable information and insight that will help you accomplish extraordinary things. If you decide to use the questionnaire, I recommend that you do so after you finish this book. Questions relating to material possessions or financial wealth are not included. If this is what you desire, you will find that by changing the way you think, feel, and behave, you can accomplish or acquire just about anything you choose. Often it is better to simply *be* first, then *do*, and finally *have*.

Here are three contemplative steps to recharting your course:

1. **Examine where you are now** (present). How do you think and feel? What are you doing? How do you think of yourself?

How do you treat yourself? What is important to you? Do you have a sense of purpose? Are you thinking, feeling, and behaving in ways that will create the future you envision? Are you going in the right direction? Are you accomplishing what you want? Are you living your life according to your values?

2. **Take a look at where you have been** (past). How does your past play a part in your life today? What were your experiences and, more importantly, what were your interpretations of them? What did you learn from the past?

3. **Imagine where you want to go** (future vision). Keep in mind not only the destination, but the kinds of experiences you want along the way. How do you want to think and feel? What do you want to do in your life? What do you want to experience? It isn't necessary to know every detail about your destination, but at least you must know the direction in which you want to travel. Remember to focus only on what is in your control.

> *You can do anything*
> *you put your mind to,*
> *as long as it's in your control.*

### Piecing Together the Puzzle

You may have no desire to change your whole life. You are probably completely satisfied with many things. Your vision of the future can be as simple as altering just one thing.

What you have done, where you have been, and what you have learned so far is the launching pad for the future. Remember that it does not matter what your experiences have been; you can change what is in your control if you really want to. Learning from the past is what is important!

As you continue to read through this book, it may seem like you are putting the pieces of a puzzle together; it's a puzzle of the map to help you find your way to "extraordinary." The more pieces you have, the clearer the overall picture becomes. If you put to use what you learn, you will gain *The Inside Advantage*.

# 4

# *Understanding Your Mind*

*Progress is impossible without change, and those who cannot change their minds cannot change anything.*

—George Bernard Shaw

Most of us are simply unaware of the extraordinary things our minds can do for us. Think about this: If you are utilizing only about ten percent of your mind's potential (which most research shows), this means that ninety percent of your inner resources are virtually untapped. I'm sure you have heard the expression "the mind is a terrible thing to waste." Put some of that extra ninety percent to work for you. Train your mind to respond in ways that help you reach your goals and enrich your life.

## Realizing Your Potential

We get so caught up in using the thinking part of the mind that we tend to ignore the inner, deeper part. The best way to realize your potential is by using both parts, the thinking, conscious mind and the inner, subconscious mind. Most people don't realize how much potential is lying dormant in our subconscious, awaiting discovery. Even fewer people utilize this knowledge to take more control over their lives and create positive changes for themselves. Maybe we just find it difficult to imagine that we can actually do it. Begin to believe that you can!

> *What my mind can conceive and my*
> *heart believe, I can achieve.*
> —CAVETT ROBERT

Ideally, we want to use our conscious minds to the fullest—being alert and thinking clearly and effectively. Even more importantly, we want to tap into the resources of the inner mind to create changes in our faulty thought and behavior patterns. We also need to effectively use both sides of our brains—the left and right hemispheres.

## Brain Hemispheres: It Takes Two

### The Left Brain

The left side of the brain is logical and analytical. It processes words and numbers. It functions when we speak, read, write, work a math problem, or listen to someone talk to us. It is hard at work when we are consciously thinking.

### The Right Brain

The right side of the brain is imaginative and creative. It processes images and sounds. It's at work when we daydream, create art, or listen to music. When we are tapping into our subconscious, the right side of the brain is functioning at its peak. It has a special relationship not only to imagery, but also to emotions.

### Dominance

Every day we use both sides of our brains, however, most of us use one side more than the other. People who are left-brain dominant mostly rely on logic—people such as accountants and engineers. Right-brained individuals are creative and are likely to be artists, actors, writers, and so forth. Which side of your brain seems to be dominant?

## Enhancing Effectiveness of Both Sides of Our Brains

Leonardo da Vinci had one of the greatest minds in the history of humankind. He used both sides of his brain. He was not only an artist and inventor, but a scientist as well. Albert Einstein, the physicist who developed the theory of relativity, is another great example of an individual who effectively used both sides of the brain. With his brain's creative right hemisphere, he was able to use his imagination to take him on a journey through the universe. With the logical left side of his brain, he developed new physics and mathematics to provide a formal framework for the images he saw.

When we allow both sides of our brains to work together, we are much more likely to reach our full potential and experience life more the way it was meant to be. The good news is that we can be both artistic and scholarly. There is no need to categorize ourselves as one or the other.

From research by Robert Ornstein of the University of California, we have learned that, when people are trained to use one side of the brain to the virtual exclusion of the other, they are relatively unable to use the other side effectively. Even more interesting about this research, according to Tony Buzman, psychologist and author of *Make the Most of Your Mind*, is the fact that ". . . when the 'weaker' of the two brains was stimulated and encouraged to work in cooperation with the stronger side, the end result was a great increase in overall ability and effectiveness."

To do anything well, both sides of the brain need to work together efficiently and effectively. How do we do that? Scientists have found that deep relaxation coordinates electrical activity between the two sides of the brain. Dr. Herbert Benson of Harvard Medical School, author of *The Relaxation Response* and *Beyond the Relaxation Response*, says that "Deep relaxation is crucial for balancing both hemispheres . . . ." The more you relax, the better your brain works.

## Brain Wave Activity

Let's take a closer look at what actually goes on in the brain. Refer to the following "Brain Wave Activity" chart. Throughout the day we experience different levels of awareness, depending upon the activity in which we are involved. These levels are characterized by different types of brain wave patterns.

**BRAIN WAVE ACTIVITY**

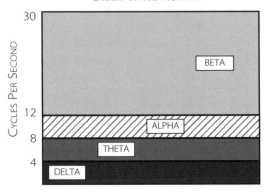

Patterns of electrical activity of the neural cells are measured by an electroencephalograph (EEG). Electrodes that are attached to a person's head pick up signals from the brain. These signals are registered on a long sheet of paper as a needle-like marker creates spikes going up and down. The number of spikes per second tells us what kind of brain wave activity a person is experiencing. Cycles per second means the number of times the brain waves are repeated each second.

Looking at the chart, we see numbers at the left. Simply stated, the higher the number, the more active the brain is, especially the conscious, thinking part. As the numbers move downward on the scale, this means the brain becomes less active. With less information to process consciously, one has less to think about.

**Beta waves** (approximately 12–30 cycles per second). Beta is the state of mind we are in when we are awake. As we go through our normal, daily activities, such as talking with friends, we are aware of many things that are going on around us. At times, even if we don't seem to be focusing specifically on something, our minds perceive our surroundings. Our survival depends on our ability to take in information from our outer environment, process it, and, if needed, respond. We almost constantly process information through our five senses: seeing, hearing, touching, smelling, and tasting.

In a beta state, we are in an alert state of mind, and our awareness is very broad. We take in a great deal of information at one time. For example, one day I started to walk across a one-way street where I typically only look in one direction for oncoming cars. As I walked out into the street, I sensed something was not right. I suddenly realized that a car was speeding toward me. It was going the wrong way! My heart started beating faster, the adrenaline pumped throughout my body, and I ran as fast as I could to get to the other side. I came within inches of being struck by the car! Fortunately, our senses work for us even without our awareness.

**Alpha waves** (approximately 8–12 cycles per second). As we are daydreaming, relaxing, drifting off to sleep, or just waking up, we are experiencing a natural, deeply relaxed state of mind and body. When we are focused on one thing, such as being caught up in the moment watching a spectacular sunset, our brains register an increased number of waves in the alpha range. If we simply close our eyes and take a few deep breaths to relax, we begin to move down the chart into an alpha state. We feel more calm, comfortable, and carefree; spending time in alpha is a very peaceful experience. Here, our awareness becomes more focused. Alpha is the link between the conscious and subconscious.

**Theta waves** (approximately 4–8 cycles per second). As the mind becomes more focused and the body continues to relax, an even deeper level of brain wave activity can be reached. Here, we are somewhere between being awake and sleeping deeply. We feel very peaceful; our muscles are completely relaxed, and our minds are carefree. Theta is the level where profound imaging and accelerated learning take place easily.

**Delta waves** (less than 4 cycles per second). Beyond theta is delta, which is the state where much of our deep sleep occurs.

**Change State = Alpha and Theta**

When our brains are registering mostly at the alpha and theta levels, we are in the ideal place for creating changes in our lives. We are more open to positive suggestions and affirmations. At these levels our minds are extremely focused and our internal awareness is very narrow, yet heightened. Vivid imaging occurs easily here. This is the perfect place to learn, recall, and program or reprogram our minds and bodies! It's where we can replace the old, negative thoughts, images, and feelings with ones that are beneficial for us. It is where we can change the faulty beliefs.

*Alpha and Theta:*
*The perfect place to go to create changes.*

We experience all of these levels every day. Each night when we are ready for sleep, our brain wave patterns will typically begin to drop from beta through alpha and theta, then down into delta. When the alarm goes off in the morning, if we are deep in sleep, our brains must become more active to process this incoming information. If we press the "snooze" button, we can linger longer. At this point we are aware that we're no longer sound asleep, nor are we fully awake yet, but drifting somewhere in between. Our muscles are still warm, loose, and relaxed and we feel very comfortable. Our mind is carefree; we are not yet thinking about what happened yesterday or what we have to do today. Life's burdens have not yet had a chance to weigh heavy on our hearts; we experience a few moments of peace of mind. Our brain wave activity changed from delta, to theta, then alpha. From here we can easily drift back to sleep (delta) or slowly wake up, in which case our brain wave patterns register more beta waves. Welcome to a new day!

## The Mind

Winston Churchill, the English political leader and author, said, "The empires of the future are the empires of the mind." If we want to go far and reach our highest potential, we need to learn more about our mental processes.

## The Conscious Mind

To help you understand more about the mind and how it works, think of the whole mind as a circle or oval, as illustrated by the following diagram. The top half represents the conscious mind. It is the judgmental, analytical, thinking part of the brain. It filters incoming information: interpreting, and either accepting, disagreeing with, or changing the information it receives, before allowing it to be filed away categorically in the subconscious.

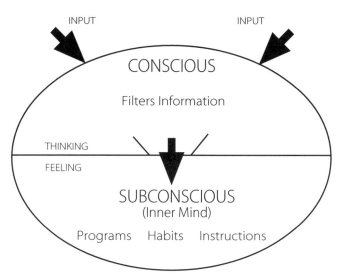

**CONSCIOUS AND SUBCONSCIOUS**

## The Subconscious or Inner Mind

The subconscious mind contains data from every experience one has ever had. Its capabilities can be compared to an extremely powerful computer that stores massive amounts of information. One of its major functions is habit formation—it quickly reminds us of whatever we repeatedly think, imagine, feel, and do.

Just as the conscious mind is the thinking part, the subconscious mind is the feeling, emotional part. It accepts and believes what it is told. It does not filter incoming information. It files it all away in perfect order, depending upon how the conscious mind perceived or analyzed it. It then returns the information into our conscious awareness, exactly as it has been stored. It makes no mistakes. It is there to serve us without hesitation. For the most part, it works automatically, unless we step inside and take control over the process.

If this is such a great system, why are we not already just the way we want to be—naturally and automatically thinking, feeling, and behaving in ways that are good for us? Well, all the subconscious has to work with is what is already stored there—our interpretations and perceptions of all our experiences right up to the present moment. Unfortunately, each of us has stored within our subconscious mind, not only the "good stuff," but also negative thoughts, images, and feelings. These can profoundly affect how we think and feel, as well as what we do. The subconscious mind is the source of what we do on a conscious level—the decisions we make, our preferences, and how we live our lives. It is also where our beliefs are stored, including our feelings about who we are and who we believe we can be.

 *We think with our conscious minds;
we feel with our subconscious.*

## Attention!

To understand more about how the mind works, let's look more closely at attention (focusing our awareness). Two aspects of attention are width (how much) and direction (where).

## Width

**Broad.** Our focus of attention can be *broad*. This is when we focus on a wide range of things almost at once, absorbing a great deal of information about what is going on around us. Our minds process, analyze, and interpret the incoming data from our surroundings. Our attention is broad when we are wide awake (beta).

**Narrow.** Our attention can also be described as *narrow*, focusing on one thing at a time, usually at a slowed pace. Whatever it is that we are concentrating on receives our full attention, whether we are relaxing, mentally rehearsing, or focusing intently on the task at hand. As we experience more brain wave activity in the alpha and theta range, we naturally focus our attention on fewer things. Likewise, when our focus becomes more narrowed, alpha and theta brain wave levels become more prevalent.

## Direction

**External.** When our attention is turned away from ourselves, we are focusing externally. We usually spend most of our time focusing this way. It is what we all have trained ourselves to do very well. We observe; we look, listen, smell, taste, and touch as we filter the information and feed it to our brains. We need this skill to survive in the world; it gives us details about our surroundings and enables us to respond accordingly. This is the process that allows us to experience our environment.

**Internal.** When we turn our attention inwardly, our focus of awareness becomes narrowed, yet heightened. Does this sound familiar? At alpha and theta brain wave levels, we are focusing our attention inwardly. The more often we focus this way on ideal concepts, images, and feelings, the easier it will be to accomplish extraordinary things.

To use our minds more effectively, we need to spend more time turning our attention inward and focusing on one thing at a time. When we are in this narrow and internal state, we are tapping into our extraordinary inner resources. By spending time in this state of mind, we can take more control over our lives, making the changes that we need and want. We can become the kind of person we want to be and create the kinds of situations we want for ourselves.

*To accomplish extraordinary things, we need to spend time focusing inwardly on what we want.*

# 5

# *We Are Who We Believe We Are*

*Many people will never accomplish extraordinary things only because they don't believe they can.*
—Cathy W. Lauro

We think, feel, and behave exactly as we have trained our minds, with or without our conscious awareness. We create the programs or habits in our subconscious minds through repetition. Anything we think over and over again, any emotional feelings we experience regularly, and anything we do repeatedly, become our natural ways of thinking, feeling, and behaving. Over time we create habit patterns that basically make us who we are.

## Our Internal Programs

These patterns are the mini-programs that work automatically without conscious effort, either for or against us. When we are dissatisfied with ourselves or our situations, it is a sign that some of our programming is faulty. Can we change the programming? Absolutely! We simply need to put forth the effort to clear new pathways in our mental jungles.

Your mind is so complex, that you could not possibly be aware of the millions of existing programs. Think of these programs as little packages of information containing thoughts, images, physical sensations, and emotional feelings on just about any subject. For example, think of a person in your life from the past or present. You may imagine his (or her) face; then you may think of your feelings about him. You remember a time together, how he smelled, and how he looked. You may hear his voice and what he said to you. All of these thoughts, images, sensations, and feelings (good and bad) are linked. You can think of them as being combined in one of the little packages (in the subconscious) with that person's name on it. Millions of subjects (packages) exist, and they are tied into an instant retrieval system, and an endlessly cross-referenced subject catalog.

## The Faulty Filtering System

It's the conscious mind that is in charge of the filtering system. It takes incoming information, analyzes and categorizes it, and allows it to pass through into the subconscious. Think of the conscious mind as a guard blocking the entrance to the subconscious, a guard who watches over incoming information, ready to process it and sort it before sending it on its way to be stored. If you try to make positive changes by forcing positive thoughts through the conscious mind, more than likely the guard will disagree with them and label them as untruths. The guard knows what is already stored in the subconscious; this is what he relies on to determine how to categorize new information.

For example, if you have low self-esteem and want to feel better about yourself, you may look into the mirror and say, "You are a good person." When your conscious mind processes that statement, the "guard" will initially reject the idea. Although that statement is not turned away (all experiences are stored), it will probably be filed in the subconscious in a package called, "Stuff I

Don't Really Believe About Myself." The conscious mind does not easily accept statements contrary to your deep feelings about who you are.

If you continue to tell the mirror's image that you are good, typically, after a short period of time, you become impatient and disillusioned. That's because you keep hearing the voice from the subconscious who reminds you of what you have believed in the past. Speaking to the mirror doesn't really seem to help much, and you stop. Nothing changes, does it?

One of the impediments to changing the subconscious is that, for the most part, you simply are not aware of the times when the negative programming occurs. Negative statements filter down into the subconscious where they get stuck. When you were a child, you had neither the knowledge nor understanding of how to interpret incoming information correctly, or at least to your advantage. If, for example, as a child you continually heard comments such as, "You're no good!" "You're stupid!" or "You'll never amount to anything," you probably interpreted those statements as true, accepted them as fact, and stored them away for future reference. When you made mistakes, those beliefs were reinforced. Over time you may have tuned in to information that continued to reinforce your perceived inadequacies. Because of this negative programming, no matter what you accomplish, you somehow feel that you're just not good enough.

Some people feel that they will never be successful at anything simply because of what psychologists term *learned helplessness*. This refers to the belief that no matter what you do, it will not matter, that somehow you are not able to create the results you want. You think, "Why even try? I can't do it." Of course, with this learned belief, you will be correct.

*What holds us back most often*
*is not who we think we are,*
*but who we think we are not.*

Often, even in adulthood, this filtering system is in poor working condition because we don't know any better. We allow the negative opinions of others to slip right down into the subconscious as accepted truths. When we do this, our self-esteem is affected. We continue to feel frustrated and unhappy; things just don't seem to be going our way.

Can you see how easy it is to get the wrong idea about our value as worthwhile human beings? Most of us have many misconceptions regarding the real truth about who we are and what we can accomplish.

What is the real truth? It is this: We can accomplish anything we set our minds to do. To do it, we may need to change our minds or we might have to recategorize the negative stuff that is already in our subconscious. It is possible!

*You can accomplish anything*
*you set your mind to.*

## Experiences, Interpretations, Perceptions, and Beliefs

The following illustration helps us understand how experiences, interpretations, perceptions, and beliefs are interrelated.

Experiences
*(Life)*

Interpretations/Perceptions
*(Conscious Mind)*

Beliefs
*(Inner Mind)*

We represent our *experiences* through thoughts, images, sensations, and feelings. There can be no doubt that we have been influenced by our past, our interactions with the world, and with others. How we think about the past, present, and future is largely determined by the information that is already stored in our subconscious minds. These pieces of information have been categorized according to our *interpretations or perceptions* up to this time. Our *beliefs* come from our interpretations and perceptions (communicated through our self-talk), especially those originating in our childhood.

As we experience life, we continue to perceive information and interpret it as we talk to ourselves. This, in turn, either creates new beliefs or reinforces old ones. What we believe influences our interpretations and perceptions; and, therefore, affects our experiences in both positive and negative ways. These are woven together like the threads that make up the fabric of our lives.

How do we make changes in our interpretations and perceptions? How do we change the way we experience life? By focusing on altering our deep beliefs about ourselves and our capabilities, we can actively and directly lay the foundation for making our lives better.

 ***Our deep beliefs are what guide us
and create our futures.***

# 6

# *Changing Our Deep Beliefs*

*What lies behind us and what lies before us are
tiny matters compared to what lies within us.*

—Ralph Waldo Emerson

For positive changes to occur in your experiences, as well as your interpretations and perceptions, you can work at deliberately changing your beliefs. You may also come to believe differently through insight.

## A Moment of Insight

A moment of insight due to a profound, emotional experience can sometimes change our lives forever. For instance, a young, deaf boy was harassed and badly beaten on a school bus. He crouched under the seat in a fetal position, crying. At that moment, he swore to himself that he would never again allow anyone to make him feel ashamed. He vowed to accept himself as he was and to make something of his life. He is now a wealthy business owner who is proud of his extraordinary accomplishments. In that one moment, he took control of his life.

If we hear a meaningful message in a speech that inspires us, we might reevaluate our old ways of thinking. After one of my presentations, the cameraman who had come to film the seminar told me that the next time we needed a camera crew, we would have to find someone else. When I asked why, he told me that he had made a decision during my presentation to close his business and go back to college. He had a moment of insight in which he believed that he could accomplish something he had always wanted to do.

When we experience either an intensely traumatic or wonderfully uplifting event, our perceptions and beliefs automatically change. When we lose a young person close to us, we may stop and reexamine life and its meaning. Some people become angry and cynical, while others view life as much more precious. These interpretations of what has happened alter what we believe in our hearts and how we experience our futures. Oliver Wendell Holmes once said, "A moment's insight is sometimes worth a life's experience."

## Insight Gained Over Time

Another way we can create changes within ourselves is to be fortunate enough to find one or more persons who will not only accept us unconditionally, but also support and encourage us over a very long period of time. In this way, whatever negative things we have learned in the past can be unlearned. If we continually receive positive feedback from someone who really cares about us, we may begin to accept and believe that what they say is true.

Unfortunately, this is not as common as the completely opposite scenario. If we hear constant criticism and experience degradation on a regular basis, over time we tend to accept a very negative view of ourselves and our capabilities.

# Conscious Effort

One thing we can do to move us along the path of change is to feed new information into our minds consciously. This includes repeating positive self-talk, or affirmations, when we are awake: "I can do this," "I am successful," etc.

> EXERCISE: **Daily Affirmations in the Mirror.** Make a commitment to yourself that, for the next thirty days starting today, you will look into your eyes in the mirror and say out loud, "I accept and love myself unconditionally."

The problem with conscious effort is that it requires persistence over a long period of time, and most people give up too soon.

# Bombard Your Inner Mind

If your desire is to change your deep beliefs, the easiest way is to influence your subconscious mind repetitively, literally bombarding it with the concepts, images, sensations, and feelings that you want to experience. In this process, your interpretations and perceptions are modified; this, in turn, alters your experiences. Although reinforcement through the subconscious is not the only way positive changes can occur, it certainly can speed up the process.

> *Bombard your inner mind with the concepts, images, sensations, and feelings you want to experience.*

### Finding Your Way into the Subconscious

How do you get to the subconscious level to make changes in the ways that you think and feel? How can you bombard it with what you want and need if the guard (at the entrance to the subconscious) is always watching? Answer: The guard is not always there; and, when he is there, he may not always be paying attention.

> ## To get inside the subconscious, distract the guard.

You want to draw the guard's attention away from his job of filtering and categorizing incoming information, somehow distracting him or gently moving him aside. This makes it easier for you to slip into the subconscious and plant new seeds of what you want to grow. These seeds contain new concepts (thoughts) and images. Bypassing the guard means that they are not first inspected, analyzed, and processed by the conscious mind. Once the concepts and images are in the subconscious, they can link with the associated physical sensations, and emotional feelings. This is what fills those "little packages" in the subconscious. *This is very important* in understanding how to put your mind to work so you can accomplish extraordinary things.

### Distracting the Guard

You can easily distract the guard at the door to the subconscious by becoming deeply relaxed. It's at this level, between waking and sleeping, that you experience more alpha and theta brain wave activity. As you become deeply relaxed, the filters between the conscious and subconscious disappear, and your mind becomes much more receptive to new information. At these deeper levels of awareness you are not processing information in the same way that you do when you are wide awake. At alpha and theta levels, thoughts and images flow freely into the subconscious mind without logical analysis and judgment. In addition, simply by using your imagination, you are able to experience related physical sensations (for example, sensing the wet sand under your bare feet as you imagine walking along the beach), and emotional feelings (self-acceptance, success, confidence, strength, peace, exhilaration, love, and so on).

### *Distract the guard with deep relaxation (alpha and theta).*

Once these new "seeds" have been planted, reinforcement of the new information on a daily basis is needed until these seeds grow to become well ingrained in the subconscious, until you naturally establish new patterns of thinking, feeling, and behaving. This process is how you change the mini-programs that have automatically worked against you. From the information packages in the subconscious, you can remove all that is limiting you and keeping you from thinking, feeling, and doing what you really want. The old, negative stuff will then be filed in another category possibly entitled, "What I No Longer Need or Want." You can deliberately change your beliefs by replacing those things with what you know will work for your advantage.

### *Relax. Then, plant new seeds and watch them grow.*

# 7

# *Relax!*

*. . . if you learn to relax deeply and do creative
visualization, you will be able to make far more
effective changes in your life than you will by
thinking, worrying, planning, and trying to
manipulate things and people.*

—Shakti Gawain

R elaxation is the first step in putting your mind to work for
you. Give yourself permission to set aside a portion of each
day to relax. If your first thought is "I don't have time!," that
should be a clear signal that relaxation is exactly what you need.
Trust that it is worth it.

Once you become relaxed, you can focus your mind, and
allow changes to occur naturally. When you are relaxed, the
body releases muscle tension and the mind calms down; you feel
comfortable and carefree. Feelings of relaxation come naturally
from many different sources. You could be walking along the
seashore or hiking in the woods on a cool autumn day. Maybe

you enjoy fishing or sitting quietly gazing into a blazing fire. No matter what your favorite forms of relaxation are, spending quiet time alone in the peacefulness of your surroundings allows you to not only recover from stress, but also to build resiliency so you can bounce back from stresses and setbacks more easily. Recreation (re-creation) provides a chance to recharge and restore yourself. We all need to make time each day just to relax and escape to serenity—mind and body.

## Relaxation of the Mind

To relax the mind, you need to let go mentally of the steady stream of thoughts that you analyze and categorize, the ones that take a lot of energy to process. Sometimes these extraneous thoughts get in the way and keep you from doing something you want to do, such as fall asleep, remember, or concentrate on one thing at a time. When you want to quiet your mind, consider any of the following exercises. It might be difficult at first, but remember, a little practice goes a long way.

> EXERCISE: **Push Thoughts Away.** With your eyes closed, focus on your breathing, in and out, through your nose or mouth, whichever way is more comfortable for you. As you do this, imagine using your hands to gently push away any distracting thoughts as they come to you. Slowly push them off to the right or left as they drift into your awareness.

> EXERCISE: **Put Your Troubles in Bubbles.** Close your eyes and imagine that each thought, image, or feeling that comes to you is encased in a bubble. See it rising into the space out in front of you. Compare its movement to a large bubble slowly rising through thick oil. Observe one bubble at a time moving upward for about five seconds, until it passes out of your visual space. Then calmly wait for the next one, observe it, and let it move on. The idea is not to describe, examine, or judge a bubble or its contents. Just observe it passively with a curious interest as to what has come to your mind at this time.

It's okay for the same bubble (with the same thought, image, or feeling) to rise several times. Take more control and slow the process down. As your mind seems to clear, you may discover that you are focusing only on the bubbles, with nothing inside. With practice you can train yourself to become more focused easily, quickly, and naturally.

In this bubble exercise, you are observing your own consciousness in a special way, while interfering with it as little as possible. Its purpose is to help you do three things: (a) establish a slow-paced mental rhythm, (b) look at each thought, image, or feeling individually without you feeling that you have to constantly find connections between them, and (c) to become more focused. This is a great exercise to play with; it will help you gain more control over your thoughts. Each of these exercises works much better when you go easy on yourself without using self-defeating statements.

## Relaxation of the Body

When you are physically relaxed, tension in your voluntary muscles is reduced, and the activities of your involuntary muscles (which control functions such as breathing, heart rate, and blood pressure) are also reduced. When your body is truly relaxed, you experience a feeling of being completely comfortable physically.

### Two Techniques for Reducing Tension

Relaxation techniques are useful for reducing both anxiety (mental) and muscular tension (physical).

1. **Send messages from your mind to your muscles.** This process involves imagining your muscles becoming relaxed. The body responds to images more directly than it does to words alone. When you want to relax your muscles, instead of only saying to yourself "relax," imagine that your body is getting a great massage. You can focus your mind on relaxing the muscles in certain parts of your body one at a time. Maybe you prefer to sense the warmth of the sun on your body to help ease the muscle

tension. Simply imagining these experiences stimulates your body to respond in very positive ways. By focusing your attention on the calming effects you will feel, you reduce muscle tension. When your body is more relaxed, it is easier for your mind to be carefree.

> EXERCISE: **Getting a Massage.** Close your eyes and imagine that the muscles in your neck and shoulders are being massaged. Feel these muscles becoming warm and loose. Sense the masseur's fingers working in small, firm circles to loosen and smooth the muscles. After only thirty seconds you will notice a change in the way your muscles feel.

2. **Send messages from your muscles to your mind.** This process involves actually moving or stretching the muscles to release tension. This sends signals to the brain that the muscles are relaxed. A common tension response is clenching of the jaws. Yawning helps to relax the jaw muscles.

Another technique that has a calming effect involves voluntarily tightening your muscles, usually one group at a time (for example, arms and fists or feet and legs), then relaxing them, releasing the tension.

> EXERCISE: **Tighten and Release.** Tighten your fists and arms. Hold for a few seconds, then let go and release the tension completely. This sends information from your muscles to your mind that you have actually let go of muscle tension.

## Deep Breathing

Slow and controlled breathing is essential to relaxation. While rapid breathing raises the heart rate and blood pressure, deep breathing brings about relaxation. It is the body's natural response to stress. For example, imagine that you are driving down the highway and a slow-moving car pulls right in front of you. You have nowhere to go, so you step on the brake as fast and as hard as you can. The adrenaline is pumping, your heart is racing, and your blood pressure has skyrocketed. You have slowed down, and you know you are going to be okay. Now what do you do?

Some people might make obscene gestures and shout a few choice words. No matter what else you do, you will probably take a very deep breath soon afterward. You don't think consciously, "Well, I need to breathe deeply now." It just happens automatically as you are releasing tension. You may take a few more deep breaths and sigh without even thinking about it. Your body's responses begin to slow down and eventually return to normal. Use this knowledge to speed the process for quick stress relief.

### Breathing Like a Baby

When you take a full, deep breath, you cause your diaphragm muscle to move down and your abdominal area will expand; this allows your lungs to fill from the bottom. This is called *diaphragmatic breathing*—using the muscle that separates the abdomen from the chest. This is how babies breathe, deeply and naturally.

> EXERCISE: **Belly Breaths.** This process may look and feel different from the way you normally breathe. You might want to put your hands on your waist to feel the movement. As you take a full deep breath, watch how your abdominal area expands, allowing room for more air. Breathe in all the air your lungs can hold (most people breathe in through their noses), then exhale slowly (typically through the mouth). Notice how you feel more relaxed after just a few deep breaths.

## Focusing

Focusing simply means concentrating on one thing at a time, such as your muscles or your breathing. It means taking more control over your thought process, much like imagining your thoughts in bubbles. Focus and relaxation are interrelated. Once you begin to relax, focusing becomes even easier; likewise, as your focus narrows, you become even more relaxed. As your brain waves reach alpha and theta, where your focus is much more narrowed, you are able to focus much more intently on whatever you choose.

 *The more you focus, the more you relax; the more you relax, the easier it is to focus.*

## Deep Relaxation

You experience deep relaxation when you allow your body to become completely relaxed and your mind is totally carefree. You are drifting peacefully somewhere between being awake and sleeping.

**Deep relaxation is especially needed when you:**
- are experiencing short-term stress
- have been under long-term stress
- have been physically active
- want to make positive changes in the way you think, how you feel (emotionally and physically), and what you do

**Regular deep relaxation:**
- builds a higher tolerance to stress and greater resiliency
- slows breathing
- promotes emotional and physical wellness
- reduces blood pressure
- helps muscles relax
- gives the body time to eliminate chemical toxins
- reduces tension headaches
- promotes deep and restful sleep
- reduces anxiety
- eliminates stressful thoughts
- helps keep things in perspective
- enhances creativity and problem-solving abilities
- stimulates coordination between the brain's left and right hemispheres

- helps with clear thinking, focusing and concentration
- reduces irritability and hostility
- enhances self-esteem and confidence
- increases feelings of inner strength and peace of mind
- gives you a sense of personal control

 *The benefits of deep relaxation carry over into all areas of your life.*

Deep relaxation is the springboard from which you can jump into your creative imagination and really get your mind working for you!

# 8

# *Imagery and Visualization*

*Imagination is the eye of the soul.*
—Joseph Joubert

I magery and visualization, for our purposes, can be used inter-
changeably. They basically refer to the same thing—creating
mental images. We can further define visualization as using our
creative imaginations to sense or experience something, anything
we choose. Visualization is creating a reality that exists in our
minds.

Without our having to think about it, most of us naturally
create images or pictures in our heads to help categorize or define
incoming information and experiences as they occur. It's like
having our own internal video recorder; what we actually experience, as well as what we create with our imagination, is recorded.
The images, along with associated thoughts, sensations, and feelings, pop into our awareness each time we reconnect in some way
with those stored experiences. If we hear a song that reminds us of
someone we used to know, instantly we are flooded with memo-

ries, and our bodies respond accordingly, either positively or negatively, depending upon our experiences with that particular person.

Whenever we daydream, we use our imaginations to create our own realities. Maybe we see an image of ourselves traveling to new place that we would like to visit, or perhaps envision that we are already successful in accomplishing a personal or professional goal.

 ***Any goal we set involves***
***visualizing the future.***

## Visualization Is a Unique Process

We all visualize in our own unique ways. Some people do not typically use visual images in their thinking. If you mentally see in image form, it may be difficult to imagine a person not being able to do that. Some of the students in my visualization classes have explained that they cannot see an apple in their minds, but instead they see the letters "a-p-p-l-e"—which, in itself, is an image. They sometimes say that they know what an apple looks like, but when they close their eyes they cannot see it. They may sense an image or scene, but cannot actually visualize it.

If you see an image, it may or may not stay in your mind's eye as long as you want. You may see an apple for a second or two, and then it's gone. If you try, you may be able to get it back for a few more seconds, only to have it disappear again. Some individuals may see the apple in such great detail that they feel that they could reach out and touch it; all of their senses come into play. They see how intense its color is. They can imagine holding it and feeling the smooth skin, touching the stem, bringing it to their noses and smelling it. Maybe they will cut it open and taste it. However, visualization can be much more than "seeing" images. (More on this will be found in Chapter 9.)

The exercises in this book are designed to help you not only understand specific concepts, but also to help develop your visualization skills in general.

While some people have problems visualizing mental images, others see very vivid inner imagery, probably the way Leonardo da Vinci or Michaelangelo did. It is said that Michaelangelo saw the image of the sculpture he was working on within the block of marble; he was just chipping away the excess to reveal the statue!

Most people can create mental images that lie somewhere in between nonexistent and very vivid. Those who claim that they can't visualize may actually be expecting too much. It's normal to see mental images as less clear and "real" than they actually are. A visual image may be only a brief fragment of an object or scene, or it may seem almost real and three-dimensional. No matter how you visualize or sense images, you can use the visualization process to make positive changes.

### The Visualization-Relaxation Connection

Generally it's easier to visualize once you are very relaxed and your awareness is very focused. Relaxation increases the blood flow to the brain's cerebral cortex, the center of visual imagery.

*The more deeply you relax, the easier it is to visualize. The more you visualize, the easier it is to relax.*

A thousand words or thoughts about visualization cannot substitute for the experience itself. With that said, let's begin to examine in more detail the extraordinary processes that go on inside our heads. Exercises in the next chapter will allow you to become more aware of different aspects of visualization.

## A Very Important Point

Your brain and your subconscious cannot tell the difference between a real event and one that is vividly imagined. The knowledge and understanding of this point is essential to using your mind more effectively.

Think about it for a moment. The brain and the subconscious cannot tell the difference between a real event that you actually experience and one that you create vividly in your imagination. This is the key to understanding why visualization helps us.

How does your mind know that you are holding this book? Your eyes see it and feed information into your brain about what you are looking at. Your hands are holding the book, and that sensory information tells your brain what you are touching. As you read silently, you "hear" your voice saying the words. If you put your nose to the pages, you can smell them. For everything we experience in reality, our minds are continually taking in sensory data and processing that information, allowing us to know what we are experiencing.

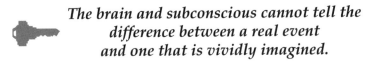

> *The brain and subconscious cannot tell the*
> *difference between a real event*
> *and one that is vividly imagined.*

The conscious mind, of course, knows the difference between reality and imagined (virtual) reality; however the subconscious does not. Remember, the subconscious is the feeling part of the mind. It stores all of your experiences—real and imagined. If you imagine something in great detail, using as many of your senses as you can to create a reality in your mind, your subconscious mind stores that information as an actual experience! What is the best way to use your imagination? With your eyes closed, through *deep relaxation and creative visualization!*

Researchers have studied what happens in the brain when we visualize, as compared to when we actually see an object. One study was done at Massachusetts General Hospital in Boston by Dr. Steven Kosslyn of Harvard. He had participants in the study imagine objects, then look at the actual objects. While they were doing this, their brains were being scanned (positron electron tomography—PET scans) to measure blood flow. What he found was that it did not matter whether the subjects were using their imaginations or actually seeing an object. Their brain scans looked almost identical; the same neural process was at work in both situations.

## Why Is This Information Important to Us?

The study's findings that neural processes are the same for real and imagined experiences provide the explanation as to how we are able to create extraordinary changes within our minds—changes that are ultimately manifested in our lives. By repetitively imagining what we want (thoughts, images, sensations, and feelings) while deeply relaxed, we convince our subconscious minds to accept and believe that what we are thinking, seeing, and feeling is true.

As we allow these positive impressions to influence us, we change the neural pathways in our minds, clearing new paths through the mental jungles. The more often we are exposed to certain thoughts, images, sensations, and feelings, the more worn that path becomes; and, the easier and more natural it is for us to follow those newly created paths.

If you want to change the way you feel about certain things, including yourself, you can. Simply relax deeply and mentally practice feeling the way you want to feel.

If you want to change the way you think, you can. Practice thinking the thoughts you want to think.

If you want to change what you do, you can. Practice mentally exactly what you want to do and how you want to do it.

If you want to create physiological changes in the body, put your mind to work for you; let your body follow your thoughts and images.

You can change the old patterns as you rewrite the mini-programs in your subconscious mind with new words, pictures, and feelings. Over time, they begin to work automatically, without conscious effort.

> ### *Retrain your mind to work*
> ### *for your advantage.*

# 9

# *Using Your Imagination*

*I shut my eyes in order to see.*

—Paul Gauguin

Individuals known for their greatness have made the most of their imaginations. Albert Einstein said, "Imagination is more important than knowledge." Stephen R. Covey, author of *The Seven Habits of Highly Effective People* and *First Things First,* advocates using the power of our creative imaginations to create enhanced quality of life. He says, "We can live out of our imagination instead of our memory." Mark Victor Hansen, co-author of *Chicken Soup for the Soul,* said in a workshop I attended that he visualized his success. He also said, "Imagery, visualization, whatever you call it, do it! It works!"

## Clarity of Visual Imagery

How well can you "see" images in your mind? If you can see them, are they clear or vague? Let's see how visual you seem to be right now:

- Can you easily recall memories and relive them in your mind?
- Do you often daydream?
- Do you like to draw or create designs?
- Are you a photographer?
- Do you enjoy looking at art?
- When you read stories, do you imagine what the characters and places look like?
- If you read music, do you play by seeing the notes in your mind, as opposed to playing by ear?
- While taking a test, do you "see" the information you studied—perhaps the place in the book or your notes?
- Can you change one image into another? (example: an apple into a ball)
- Can you describe a friend's appearance?
- When giving directions, do you mentally see those streets and traffic lights that you mention?
- Do you learn best through reading, writing, and looking at graphs and charts? (as opposed to lectures, verbal instructions, or by hands-on learning)

The more "yes" answers you give, the more visual you are at this point. If you are very visual it is more likely that your brain's right hemisphere is dominant. However, even if you are mostly "left-brained," you may still experience vivid imagery. Remember that each of us is unique in our visualization process.

## Developing Visualization Skills

Below are several exercises to help you become more aware of how you are currently using your imagination; at the same time you will be developing your visualization skills.

EXERCISE: **Chair and Dog.** Let's start with an exercise that uses several different aspects of visualization. Read this paragraph, then close your eyes and take a few deep breaths. Next, imagine a white chair, any kind of white chair you want. See what pops into your head naturally. If you don't like the chair that happens to appear, change it. Is it made of cloth, leather, wood, or something else? Go ahead and close your eyes and use your imagination now.

Think about what just happened in your mind. Notice first of all, if a white chair popped up easily or if you had to work to create one. Did you see it, or did you sense a chair in some way? If you saw an image and it was one you did not like, did you change it to another? Was it easy to do that? Ask yourself if it seemed like a two-dimensional photograph, flat and still, or did it appear more realistic, as if you could reach out and touch it? Were you able to hold onto the image for as long as you wanted, or did it appear and then disappear before you were ready to let it go? As you become more aware of how you visualize, you can intentionally take more control in creating images.

After reading this paragraph, close your eyes again and put a little white dog in the middle of that chair. Put a red bow on the dog, then get the dog to move in some way, wag its tail or make it jump up and down. Then change the white dog to black. Listen to it bark. See if you can make these changes easily or if you have to put forth extra effort to make them happen. Go ahead and try it.

## Questions To Ask

Was the white dog one you have known or seen before? If it was a dog you owned, did you experience feelings about the dog? Could you make it sit in the chair? Were you able to add the bow? Was it red? Was the dog wearing a collar? Did you hear it bark? Could you get it to move? Were you able to change it to black, or did you see that it had spots instead? Maybe to change the color you had to change dogs. Did you notice anything else about this scene that popped up or that you added naturally?

No matter how you experienced this exercise, know that your mind is always doing its best for you. Be patient if you don't visualize the way you want to yet. Visualization is a skill that you can develop over time with practice. What is important to realize is that, no matter how images come to you, you can learn to step inside your mind (become an active participant) and take more control over them. In this way you take charge of the inner processes and force your mind to work for you. You have a tremendous amount of control over your mind—much more than you may have previously thought.

 ***Step inside your mind and take control.***

## Photographic or Video Images?

One type of mental image is similar to a photograph—still and two-dimensional. If you initially perceive images this way, you can add dimension to them by creating movement—animation—by several still images or "photos" flashing in your mind. Remember that imagery can also be like an internal video, a mental movie, in which you are watching an event with action occurring naturally. You may even see yourself playing a character in your video. You know that some photos and videos that you take with your camera turn out bright, clear, and sharp; others may be dark, cloudy, and a bit out of focus. The same thing goes for mental images.

## Controlling Visual Imagery

Visual control has to do with manipulating the images in your mind: changing them in some way, replacing one image with another; adjusting the focus or brightness, or perhaps causing action or movement. If a white chair popped into your mind and you didn't care for the one you first saw, maybe you changed it to be more to your liking. When you made the dog wag its tail or jump, you were taking visual control. Following this next section, you will find a few more exercises to help you practice taking more control over images. You may want to play with an image of your own and see how much control you have over it.

## Colors

Until just a few years ago, I could only see images in my mind as black, white, and shades of gray. I suppose I never really tried to see colors before. They did not come naturally to me. When I learned that it was possible to develop an inner sense of color, I spent some time trying to add this dimension to my imagery. With my eyes closed and while deeply relaxed, I focused on what different colors looked like. I sensed them in a way, but I had not seen them with my eyes closed. After I made several attempts at this, suddenly from the gray dullness splashed a bright lime-green, much like wet paint on the inside of my eyes. Wow! What an exciting moment! From then on I was able to quickly add many more colors to paint my mental scenery.

We can make our mental images more realistic if we are able to sense color. A blazing yellow and orange fire seems hotter to us than black and white; blue flames burn even hotter. We know these things intellectually; and, if we can see them in our minds, this helps to create a more vivid reality.

If you see colors with your mind's eye, you may find that they appear naturally. However, you can create the colors you choose or change the ones that automatically come to you.

Colors evoke emotional responses and can communicate immediate physiological effects—sometimes even more powerfully than words. Play with different colors in your mind as you do the exercises in this book; see which ones seem to work well for your specific purposes. With practice, you will find that it's much easier to use your imagination creatively to visualize what you need and want.

The following is a list of a few colors and some of their psychological or symbolic associations:

| | |
|---|---|
| *Black* | nothingness, passive, holding back, evil, elegant |
| *Blue/Green* | contentment, calms the nervous system, retreats from the eye |
| *Pink* | healthy, natural |
| *Purple* | healing, sophisticated, successful |
| *Red* | strong, active, passionate, bold, exciting, moving forward |
| *White* | purity, sterility, peace |
| *Yellow* | lively, breezy, cheerful, easily noticed |

## More Clarity and Control Exercises

Let's try a few more exercises designed to enhance your visual clarity and control.

> EXERCISE: **Color the Dog Purple.** Do you remember changing the white dog in the white chair to black? Close your eyes and see if you can change the white dog into one that is purple. You may really have to put your mind to work on this one.
>
> *Clarity.* Was the white dog clear, vague, or barely visible?
>
> *Control.* Could you create an image (a purple dog) that does not exist in reality?
>
> *Clarity.* If you were able to change it to purple, was it clear, vague, or barely visible?

Don't feel bad if you couldn't do this exercise yet; many people have a difficult time imagining a purple dog. Most of us have to work at visualizing images that don't exist in reality. It may be helpful to think of a purple cartoon character or stuffed animal.

> EXERCISE: **Colored Ball.** If you want to practice developing your visualization skills by using color, this will be fun and helpful. Close your eyes and imagine a ball of any color you choose. It can be large or small, soft or hard; it is entirely up to you. Whatever color it is, change it to another color. Repeat this as often as you like until you feel that you have as much control as you want.
>
> EXERCISE: **The Galloping Horse.** After reading this paragraph, close your eyes, take a few deep breaths, and relax. Then imagine that you are sitting in a saddle on a horse. Feel the leather saddle underneath you and your feet in the stirrups. Hold on to the reigns and get the horse to start moving forward, slowly at first. Next, make the horse gallop across an open field. Sense that the horse is going faster and faster as you ride; you are bouncing up and down in the saddle. After a short time, make the horse stop as fast as you can. Go ahead and do this now.
>
> Then, with your eyes open, think about what just occurred in your mind:

*Clarity.* How vivid was this scene? Could you really imagine being there, touching the horse, seeing the open field and the horse's mane flowing in the wind?

*Control.* Were you in control of the horse, or was it the other way around? Did you make him gallop faster? Could you sense the animal's speed? Did it stop quickly when you wanted it to, or did it take a while? Are you beginning to gain more of a sense of control?

EXERCISE: **Inside the Realm of Possibilities.** Close your eyes, take a few deep breaths, and:

1. Imagine a Dalmatian puppy, white with spots. You could imagine a whole litter and the mother, too. Then, one at a time or all at once, remove all their spots.

2. See a big brown or black bear and put horns on the top of its head.

3. Put a human face on a squirrel in the park. Smile at him and watch him smile back at you.

4. Look into a mirror and see yourself at your ideal weight. Your muscles are firm and toned, and your waist is trim. You are wearing a great outfit, looking healthy, and feeling energetic, confident, and happy.

These are just a few examples of using your creative imagination in ways that are different from our normal thinking. If you need to change the way you think, maybe you need to stretch your imagination. Give it a nudge to get it in better working condition. Have some fun creating your own images. Let your child-like imagination run wild!

 *Soar on the wings of your imagination!*

## Other Senses: Taste, Smell, Hearing, and Touch

Remember, we defined visualization as using our creative imaginations to sense or experience things. Vision is not the only sense we can use in visualizing. Visualization creates a reality in our minds by using our senses—the more senses used, the more powerful the visualization.

The following mental exercises involve using your senses other than vision. Feel free to add your own ideas and play for a while in your mind.

### EXERCISE: **The Senses.**

1. Close your eyes, take a few deep breaths, and imagine smelling one of your favorite foods. If you need to use a fork or spoon, sense the utensil in your hand. If it is hand-held food, feel it with your fingers. Imagine putting the food into your mouth. Sense its temperature. Feel the texture as you chew and taste it. Is it sweet, sour, bitter, salty, or a combination? Does it make a sound when you chew it? Allow yourself to experience and enjoy the delicious flavors and aromas.

2. Use your mind to hear the faint sound of what seems to be wind chimes in the distance. Hear the sounds become louder as if they are moving closer to you. Take a deep breath, let your body relax, and enjoy the peaceful tones.

3. Imagine that you are touching a piece of velvet. Rub your hands over it, and feel how soft and smooth it is. Feel the fibers move under your fingers.

If you have trouble creating specific images, then just sense whatever is easy and natural for you at the time. You will find that you enhance your visualization skills each time you use your imagination. Remember that the more deeply you relax while you are doing these exercises, the easier it will be to focus in greater detail. Using your senses fully will make your imaginary experiences seem more realistic.

Creating scenes in your mind that seem almost real, is an important part of gaining *The Inside Advantage.* Did you notice that once you took control over your thoughts and images, you changed the way you felt? That may be all you need at times—to feel better, more calm and carefree. Learn to put your imagination to work for immediate needs or long-term goals.

*The more related sensory information*
*we feed into our brains, the more realistic*
*our imagined experiences become.*

### Anchoring

Another useful technique that can help you change the way you think and feel is called *anchoring.* It refers to the process of associating an internal response with an external trigger. This is similar to what psychologists call *classical conditioning.* We learn to associate those things that are linked. When one is present, the other follows. Anchors occur naturally all the time. Think about what happens when you hear a particular old song. You may begin to feel sad because it's the song that was playing when your lover broke up with you. No matter how much time has passed, when you hear that song, your heart seems to break all over again, doesn't it? The song (external trigger) and those emotional feelings (internal response) are linked in a "little package" in your subconscious mind. Remember that millions of these packages contain links that were created without your awareness.

You can use this information to your advantage by deliberately creating links that work for you automatically. Emotional and physiological states can be triggered without your having to think about it consciously.

When you are deeply relaxed, and using your imagination to experience certain positive thoughts, images, sensations, and feelings, use some sort of triggering device to make the connection. Triggers might include such things as smelling a chosen scent, holding a special object, or thinking or saying a particular word. Use your imagination to come up with something that is right for you. The trigger is then linked in your subconscious with those same mental, emotional, and physical responses (mind and body). You will want to reinforce this for about 21–30 days; then, whenever you need to, use the trigger to automatically bring about those same responses.

Use your new anchors to take control of your moods. For instance, when you're upset, change your mood with a positive anchor. This might involve taking a deep breath and thinking the word "calm."

**10**

# Effective Visualization

*Vision is the art of seeing things invisible.*

—Jonathan Swift

Visualizations can be either active or receptive. *Active imagery* involves mental pictures that you deliberately construct. When you use active imagery, you take charge of your thoughts. For instance, if someone were to ask me to mentally picture a house—inside and out—that I would like to build for myself, it would take much effort on my part. I could think of all sorts of styles and decorations. I may think of one thing, then change it to something I liked more. I would be creating the images intentionally. Active visualization requires that you participate.

Receptive visualization happens when you wait quietly, passively, and let images come to you automatically. The exercises in the previous chapter involved both types of visualization. When you initially thought of the chair, the dog, and the horse, maybe specific images just popped into your head without much effort. You were the observer of what came to you—that is *recep-*

*tive visualization*. Perhaps the dog you visualized was your pet—you didn't have to think much about it because it was familiar. If someone were to ask me to think of a white dog, I would automatically think of Jacques, the white poodle I had for seventeen years. An image of him would quickly and naturally come to me. Receptive visualization requires that you observe.

Are you beginning to see a difference? Active and receptive visualizations are very closely linked when we process information and we use both almost simultaneously. Most of us are not aware of the difference between the two unless we stop and think about it. The idea here is to take notice of the process. Slow down long enough to become aware of whether pictures just appear automatically, or whether you actively construct images. Then, once you have an image in your mind, you can either accept it as it is, reject it, or change it by actively manipulating it in any way you want.

*Active visualization requires
that you participate.
Receptive visualization requires
that you observe.*

## A Personal Experience:
## Finding Strength and Peace

A personal visualization experience provides a perfect example of imagery that is both *active* and *receptive*. Years ago when I felt very sad, helpless, and hopeless, I sat with my eyes closed and began taking slow deep breaths, allowing my body to become very relaxed. I moved from the waking beta state to a much more focused state of alpha-theta. I went to a special place in my mind, seeking comfort.

The scene was a grassy clearing with green trees all around. I arrived at this place from a path winding through the forest. There was a gazebo with flowers growing around it. In the distance another path from the forest opened to the clearing. There was a nearby shallow stream of clear water. I sat down on the soft grass and put my bare feet into the cool water. The sun was shining down from the blue sky; I could feel the warmth of the sun on my shoulders and back. I listened to the sounds of the birds in distant trees. I saw a bluebird fly by. I sipped some iced tea with lemon. This was a place I came to get away and renew my mind, body, and spirit.

That was *active visualization*. I created it all in my mind and I used my senses to make it seem even more realistic.

In my sorrow, I sat there with such a heavy heart, and I asked for help. To me, the source of help was the creative power of the universe, whatever you might call it. I asked to be given what I needed at that time to help me feel better. Then I sat quietly and waited. Soon after, I noticed my maternal grandmother to my left, coming from the path on the other side of the clearing. I had not seen her so clearly since she died in 1974. She was very special to me. I was surprised and so happy to see her!

That was *receptive visualization*—her image came to me without my direct, conscious control. I watched that scene unfold as opposed to actively creating it. I did not decide to put her in that scene; she just appeared. She was smiling and walking barefoot toward me. I noticed that she was carrying a white-tipped wooden cane, the kind she used when I was a child many years before her death. She sat down next to me on the water's edge and, like me, put her feet into the water. I remember asking her, "Maw-Maw, I thought after we died our spirits wouldn't need things like wheelchairs or canes." She laughed and, in her raspy voice, said, "Oh, Honey, this cane isn't for me; I brought it for you."

I began to cry (in reality), tears streaming down my cheeks, because instantly I understood the symbolism she had brought me. The cane meant support and strength, and I knew somehow that I would be okay again. Hugging her and not wanting to let go, I thanked her for coming to me and bringing comfort, love, strength, and peace of mind. I watched as she walked away; she turned, waved, and disappeared into the forest.

From the moment my grandmother made her appearance up until this point, I was experiencing receptive visualization. I did not intentionally create an image of her in my mind; rather she drifted into the scene naturally.

As I took control of the images once again, the visualization then became active. I stood up, walked into the gazebo and leaned the cane against the wall. I decided to keep it there so I could see it any time I returned to this place in my mind. I took a few deep breaths, slowly opened my eyes, and returned to what seemed like a different reality.

After that experience I knew that I could cope with my situation because I felt a deep sense of inner peace and strength. Through active and receptive imagery I changed the way I felt. To me, that was extraordinary!

Knowing how to use active and receptive visualization can help you feel better about yourself and your situations. Ask for what you need and want; and, if you believe deep in your heart, if you have faith that you will receive it, chances are you will.

## Trusting Your Inner Mind

In my work as a personal success coach, time and time again I have witnessed how individuals are able to use their minds to come up with exactly what they need at certain points—answers and insights to help them move forward more easily. Throughout this journey inward, the idea is not only to use active visualization to create whatever you choose, but also to allow your mind to be receptive to what you need.

Once you allow yourself to step back and get out of your own way, you will discover more about how your mind can work for you automatically. Ideas, images, and feelings are revealed naturally. You will be fascinated at how incredible the inner journey can be. When you step inside your mind, it is possible to accomplish extraordinary things, programming success in any number of ways. I have personally seen individuals heal not only their pain and sorrow, but in many cases, their lives as well. It is a matter of trusting and relying on your inner mind to be the instrument that provides what you need.

# Perspective Awareness

Another aspect of visualization is perspective, or viewpoint. There are two different perspectives from which a person can imagine.

When you look through your own eyes, when you are involved in the scene you are imagining, you are using an **associative** perspective. It is how you experience life; your senses are directly involved. Your feelings—emotional and physical—are strong and real.

When you observe yourself from outside the scene—as if you are watching yourself in a movie, video, or play—this is the **dissociative** perspective. This is not how you experience life in reality.

### *Associative = The Participant*
### *Dissociative = The Observer*

EXERCISE: **A Happy Memory.** Close your eyes after reading this sentence and think of a happy memory for a few moments.

Now become aware of how you sensed that scene. What perspective did you automatically use? Were you actively involved as a participant, looking through your own eyes, or were you watching yourself from a distance?

EXERCISE: **An Unpleasant or Sad Memory.** This time close your eyes and briefly think of an unpleasant or sad memory; then allow your eyes to open.

Notice how it appeared in your mind. Was it from an associative or dissociative perspective? Become aware of how you felt, emotionally and physically.

When re-experiencing the past, most of us have a natural tendency to visualize both positive and negative images associatively. We are involved as participants, seeing through our own eyes, just the way those experiences were initially processed and recorded in our minds. Usually when we dissociate from the scene, we have a sense of detachment. Our emotional and physical feelings are more neutral. (Chapter 12 discusses the use of dissociation for stress relief.)

## Switching Perspectives

These following exercises are designed to help you take more control over the process of switching from one perspective to another.

> EXERCISE: **Coughing.** Close your eyes and imagine yourself coughing from the associative perspective. Sense that your body is moving. Imagine yourself putting your hand to your mouth, feeling the air come out, and listening to the sound your cough makes. Experience it in your mind just the way you would normally cough. Then see if you can switch to dissociate yourself from the cough by seeing an image of yourself coughing. It may help to imagine seeing yourself on a television or movie screen; perhaps you imagine that you are watching yourself on stage.

Notice the differences in the physical and emotional responses caused by the two perspectives. When you are watching yourself cough, there is no direct connection between you and the cough. You see it and perhaps having an opinion about it, but you are not experiencing the physical sensations of coughing.

> EXERCISE: **Back in the Saddle Again.** Do you remember imagining yourself galloping on that horse? Close your eyes again and re-experience that. Feel the saddle underneath you. Your feet are in the stirrups, and you're holding on to the reigns as he gallops across the open field. Then, switch perspectives and watch yourself from a distance. See the beauty of the animal, its mane flowing in the wind. Watch yourself bouncing up and down on the saddle. Afterwards, open your eyes.

Again, notice the differences in your reactions to the two perspectives. Regardless of the way you naturally see pictures in your mind, you have the ability to change from one perspective to another. It is just a matter of consciously doing this.

*Associate to enhance positive feelings.*
*Dissociate to reduce negative feelings.*

## Tips for Effective Visualization

1. **Create images that are important to you.** Think about what you are trying to accomplish and choose images that have meaning for you.

2. **Focus on positive thoughts and images.** Focus on what you want, rather than on what you do not want. If I tell you, "Don't think of pink elephants," what do you think of? Pink elephants!

3. **Use the present tense.** When we work to create positive changes, it is important to understand that the subconscious mind functions only in the present moment. It makes no difference whether we are focusing on the past or future—to the subconscious, the only time that exists is now. For example, rather than thinking "I will feel fine," use "I am feeling fine." Use statements in the present tense, as if they are already true. In your mind, create the ideal future as you want it to be, then bring that image into the present moment. Sense the situation as fact, as if it has already occurred. *This is a very powerful piece of information!*

4. **Intensify with different senses.** Use your imagination to sense all the details needed to create a "real" situation. Intensify your images and scenes by using as many senses as you can—see, hear, touch, smell, and taste.

5. **Draw on your emotions.** Allow yourself to emotionally experience a situation or event in your mind, to experience the feelings associated with the thoughts and images you create. To do this effectively, use the associative perspective; be the participant. Our emotions provide enormous power to create change for ourselves. Feel with emotion!

6. **Energize.** Physically feel in your body the sensations you want to experience. Get those chemical and electrical impulses

going as your mind and body work together to produce your desired results. Get moving mentally!

## How Visualization Works

Each one of us who has had an experience of accomplishing something extraordinary through the use of visualization has our own ideas about how it worked. Mike Samuels, in his book *Seeing With the Mind's Eye: The History, Techniques and Uses of Visualization*, suggests that from a psychologist's viewpoint it could be theorized this way: "... fixing an image in the mind stimulates the subconscious to be continuously alert to situations that will further the goal and signal the conscious mind to assertively act in those situations." He also adds, "A religious person might say that it is God hearing a person's prayer and answering it." Perhaps it's both.

 *Visualization is the ultimate tool.*

# 11

# *The Mind-Body Connection*

*The whole of science is nothing more than
a refinement of everyday thinking.*

—ALBERT EINSTEIN

Perhaps the idea of a connection between the mind and the body first came to Western culture through television and movies. Do you remember the TV series *Kung Fu* and how it related to the power of the inner mind? Think about the movie *Star Wars*—it provided the idea of a "force" being with us. George Lucas, the producer, was influenced by ideas from Zen Buddhism, and by Joseph Campbell, author of *The Hero with a Thousand Faces*.

In the 1960s, transcendental meditation was just beginning to flourish in the United States. Since then, yoga and other body meditations have become increasingly popular. A growing number of people in this country are becoming interested in, and are more open to, this notion of a connection between the mind and body. In recent years, many books have been written, and documentaries and television specials produced about how the mind can alter the body.

## Your Body Follows Your Thoughts

Emotions are not only psychological, but physical as well. As we think thoughts and see images in reality or in our imaginations, our bodies respond physiologically. Our bodies follow our thoughts, regardless of whether we are actually experiencing an event or only imagining it. Depending upon how we perceive those thoughts and images, positive or negative, our bodies respond accordingly. Whenever we feel emotions, our bodies are automatically involved chemically and electrically.

*The mind leads;
the body follows.*

Let's do a few exercises to show how the mind can influence the body.

EXERCISE: **Hands Up! Hands Down!** Put your feet flat on the floor and place your hands on your lap. Look upward without raising your head (this helps you experience more alpha brain waves) and take a few belly breaths. As your eyes become tired, let them close naturally. Take a full, deep breath, and let go of muscle tension. Allow your mind to drift peacefully as your body becomes more deeply relaxed.

Raise both hands out in front of your chest. Imagine that your right hand is warm, limp, and very relaxed. Sense that it feels very heavy, too heavy to keep holding up like this. It's almost as if someone were pushing it down. Begin to allow your right hand to actually move down slowly.

Take a full, deep breath and exhale slowly as you continue to feel the pressure and the heaviness in your right hand. At the same time imagine that your left hand feels very light, almost weightless. Sense that a balloon filled with helium is tied to your wrist. Feel the balloon raising your left hand higher and higher as your hand grows lighter. Allow your left hand to move naturally as you feel the upward tug of the balloon. Take a deep breath and open your eyes. Quickly notice where your hands are.

If you used your imagination even a little, your right hand should be lower than your left. We are simply directing our bodies to follow our minds. We imagine a situation, and our bodies tend to follow along. Let's do another experiment to demonstrate how your body follows your thoughts:

EXERCISE: **Tasting a Lemon.** Close your eyes and imagine that you are in your kitchen at the counter. In front of you is a chopping board. You are holding a sharp knife in one hand and a big yellow lemon in the other. Feel the weight of the lemon in your hand. Sense its coolness and texture. In your mind, put the lemon on the board and slice it in half. Pick up half and squeeze it a little. Smell how fresh it is. It's very juicy. Next, hold it up to your mouth, bite into it, and suck the juice.

Did you get a tingling in your salivary glands? Did your mouth pucker up? You created a reality by using your imagination. Our bodies physically feel what we create in our minds. We experience an event physically, as if it actually happened, because of our thoughts and images.

EXERCISE: **Imagining and Creating Movement.** Tie a small weight of some kind to a string or filament (for example, a lead weight on a fishing line). With your elbow resting on a tabletop and your hand up in the air, let the string hang over your index finger as the weight dangles about an inch above the table. (You may keep your eyes open for this one.)

Without moving your fingers or your arm, begin to imagine the weight moving back and forth, from left to right, then right to left, and so on. Concentrate and focus your attention as you visualize the weight continuing to move back and forth. Allow your mind and eyes to trace a straight path in which the weight will move. The more you visualize and use your imagination, the more it will move.

Now visualize the weight stopping. Take your time to concentrate and mentally see the weight simply hanging there.

Keep your arm and hand in the same position, with the weight hanging motionless. This time imagine the weight making a clockwise revolution around an imaginary circle with a diameter of about two or three inches. Concentrate and visualize it moving around and around. Want it to happen, and it will.

Even with no visible action occurring, your muscles respond to the power of your mind as you visualize movement of the weight. Low-level sequences of electrical impulses are actually sent to your muscles, and movement occurs. Motor neurons in the muscles are activated simply by imagining the movement of the weight. Your mind creates movement in your muscles which, in turn, causes the weight to move. Your body follows your thoughts and images. Think of the possible applications! We are used to training our bodies with physical conditioning, but we tend to put little effort into mental preparation. Remember that visualizing not only prepares the mind for an activity, but also the body.

*You can train your body to prepare for activities in advance by visualizing your performance in great detail.*

## Your Autonomic Nervous System

To more fully understand the mind-body connection, it's important to mention the body's autonomic nervous system (ANS). This system controls involuntary functions such as heart rate, breathing, body temperature, and digestion. The ANS adjusts these functions continuously in order to meet our changing environment. It is actually composed of two separate systems, the *sympathetic* and the *parasympathetic* systems. One of the main jobs of these systems is to regulate the body's response to stress. (Learn more about how to deal with stress in Chapters 12 and 13.)

### The Sympathetic System

When your body is under stress, regardless of the source, a number of physiological changes occur. The sympathetic system kicks in, preparing your body to meet the perceived challenge. Your heart rate and blood pressure go up, and you begin breathing faster. You get a boost in your energy supply as your liver dumps glucose into your bloodstream. Your muscles become tense, and your digestion slows or stops; you are ready to spring into action. Your pupils dilate and eyeballs flatten for distant vision.

Why does your body react this way? The physical response stems from primitive times when our early ancestors had to deal with physical threats, such as fending off hungry animals. The appropriate reaction was to fight to the death or try to run away. In this "fight or flight" response, the brain has only a few seconds to prepare us for action. It goes to work by flooding the body with chemical messengers that cause all this to happen instantaneously.

These physiological reactions from the sympathetic nervous system, in response to fight-or-flight situations, helped humankind survive back then. Today, we still need our bodies to go to work for us automatically in life-or-death situations. Fortunately, however, we don't encounter life-or-death situations on a regular basis.

Most of our threats these days come to us in the form of emotional challenges. Negative physical changes in our bodies can come from many sources. One example is verbal confrontation; when we argue with someone, our blood pressure rises, we breathe quickly, and our muscles become tense. Our bodies are affected negatively because of our own internal dialogues—what we say to ourselves about what is happening. If we interpret a situation as a threat, we physically respond to our own thoughts and images.

*The body makes no distinction between*
*a physical and an emotional threat,*
*real or imagined.*

## The Parasympathetic System

During calm and balanced emotional states, the parasympathetic system takes control of the body's autonomic functions. Your heart rate slows down, respiration becomes slow and steady, digestion speeds up, your pupils become smaller, and your eyeballs become more convex for close vision.

The good news is that you can take control of bodily functions you may have previously thought were uncontrollable. You can slow your heart rate, lower your blood pressure, change your body temperature, and possibly much more than you might have ever imagined. You do this by using your mind to change your thoughts and images. When you change the way you think, you can change how you feel. Chapter 14 deals with the mind-body connection as it relates to wellness.

# 12

# *Stress Relief*

*I have experienced some terrible things in my life,
and some of them have actually happened.*

—MARK TWAIN

In one form or another, we all experience stress. Life is stressful. There will always be a need to cope with what life hands us and, the more we know about what we can do to help ourselves, the better off we will be. Our thoughts, images, and feelings about a particular situation determine our level of stress. Situations or others can "invite" us to feel stressed, but we are the ones who decide whether or not to accept those invitations. When we take more control over the processes that go on inside our heads, we are able to cope with stress far better than we have previously thought.

One of the most common requests I receive is for help with stress relief. A favorite program is "Let Go, Lighten Up and Get On With It™," which says exactly what we must do in order to move forward.

*Let go of those things we cannot change,
let go of negative energy, live life more
joyfully and successfully, and do it now!*

Each of us has different needs that must be considered when developing stress reduction strategies. That's why, prior to presenting a stress management training program for the retail chain Dillard's, Inc., I conducted a nationwide survey of their sales managers; this allowed me to tailor the program to effectively address their specific needs. Mangers in every store across the country were exposed to *The Inside Advantage.* If you shop at Dillard's, you may notice that their employees seem to be not only friendly and helpful, but also calm; they know how to handle daily pressures, both on the job and at home.

## Stress and Health

The word *stress* comes from the Latin root *stringere* (pronounced "string gary") meaning "to draw tight." Isn't that what we do when we feel stressed? Our muscles contract, and we feel tense. We experience headaches, muscle spasms, and a host of related physical problems. Research continues to link stress to many illnesses. It's estimated that at least three-fourths of visits to physicians are stress-related. The more stress we experience, the more likely a candidate we are for heart attacks, high blood pressure, and other illnesses as our immune systems become exhausted. This is especially true if we experience high levels of stress over a long period of time. In spite of the scientific evidence linking stress to health problems, most people don't believe that stress increases health risks for themselves. We need to realize just how much damage can be done to our bodies by stress; only then will we make an effort to reduce its negative effects.

Scientific experiments have demonstrated that, when we are experiencing intense, negative emotions such as fear or anger, powerful and lethal toxins are manufactured inside our bodies. Guinea pigs were injected with blood samples taken from individuals experiencing these feelings. The animals died in less than two minutes! Imagine what these toxins do to our bodies, especially over time.

Every thought you have affects your body's chemistry within a split second. Do you remember how you felt when you were driving on the highway and a slow-moving car suddenly pulled in front of you? A shock wave went through your whole system. Your mind caused your body to react instantly. When you experience a stressful situation and perceive it as a threat, your body gears up for action. If you don't run away or fight, your body is left in a highly-charged state with no physical release.

Without thinking about it, we may release that pent-up negative energy in a variety of ways: biting our fingernails, clenching our teeth, jiggling change in our pockets, or even verbal or physical abuse of others. Some individuals literally pull their hair out! Think about your current outlets for releasing the negative energy that comes from stress. Trust that you can change habits like these if you really want to. (The "Extraordinary Changes Questionnaire" in the Appendix will help.)

Normally, once a threat is over, our bodies gradually bring themselves back into balance. However, we may not have a chance to recover fully if we have little or no release, especially if we continue to experience stress over a long period of time from a variety of sources. When we spend much of our day in a state of "red alert," we use up our resources for staying healthy. Stress hormones, if not burned up with activity, build up in the blood to damage vessels and clog arteries, leading to heart disease or heart attacks. Cortisol is a powerful stress hormone released by the adrenal glands; long-term exposure to abnormally high levels of this hormone can also damage brain cells.

A report by The International Labor Organization entitled, *Job Stress: The 20th Century Disease,* estimates that the cost of job stress in the United States is $200 billion annually. Costs are related to reduced productivity, absenteeism, compensation claims, health insurance, and medical expenses for related diseases such as high blood pressure and heart attacks. It makes good sense for businesses to do all they can, not only to reduce these unnecessary costs, but also to help employees manage their stress.

## Managing Stress with Release and Recovery

To help you manage stress more effectively, use release and recovery. Here's how to take control and let go of the physical tension and negative energy, and speed up the process of returning to a calm state of mind and body.

**Release** means physically moving your body in some way—using your muscles to do what your body has naturally prepared for in its fight-or-flight response. Give your body what it wants. Go with the natural flow of what your body needs to do. This is a great reason to exercise regularly!

The next time someone pulls in front of you on the road and your body is flooded with adrenaline, after you know you are safe, squeeze the steering wheel over and over. Squeeze and let go as many times as you need to help you release the physical tension. This exercise will help you let go of some of that negative energy immediately. Forget about the other driver; instead, focus on releasing your stress in a positive way. Then, take time to recover.

**Recovery** is returning to a calm and healthy state of mind and body. To lessen the harmful effects of stress, it is important that you recover as quickly as possible. Recovery can be attained by means as simple as taking a few belly breaths. You may want to become very quiet and still as you mentally guide your mind and body to feel more relaxed. Harvard research has shown that, after thirty days of deeply relaxing for at least twenty minutes a day (even ten minutes twice a day), you build a higher resistance to stress. You will feel much more calm and in control throughout the day. The more you practice deep relaxation, the less time you will need for recovery in any situation.

*To find stress relief, it is extremely important to incorporate periods of release and recovery into your daily routine.*

# Managing Stress by Manipulating Negative Images

Stress can come from filling our minds with negative thoughts and images of the past or imagining negative situations that might happen in the future. When we do this, we cause ourselves needless harm—mentally, emotionally, and physically.

Unfortunately, the more often you think about things in a negative way, the more that becomes your normal pattern of thinking. When you remember and dwell on negative past events, sometimes you produce more stress than the original situation ever did. When you worry about the future, you may cause yourself more stress than the actual event ever would have caused.

The good news is that you can simply think of something else more pleasant, or you can learn to manipulate any negative image or scene that comes to mind so that it will not create a stressful response.

Let's look at two additional practical techniques that will help with stress relief—replacement and dissociation. These techniques allow you to manipulate negative images to help change the way you feel.

## Replacement

With **replacement**, you substitute one image or scene for another. If what you are thinking is not beneficial to you, then stop thinking about it! Replace the negative thought with something more positive.

EXERCISE: **The Charging Bull.** Read this paragraph, then play with this scene in your mind. Close your eyes, take a deep breath, and imagine that you are alone in the middle of a wide, open field. Way off in the distance you see a mean-looking bull. You're wearing red. Make sure the bull is facing you. See him snorting and scraping the ground with his hooves; you know he's about to charge at you. Get him to start running toward you. Make him run faster and faster; and, before he gets to you, change him into a beau-tiful, white dove, and make it fly up overhead. Then open your eyes.

## What Does This Tell Us?

After you've done the charging bull exercise, think about what you experienced. If you clearly imagined it, your heart may have started beating a little faster. Your body was following your thoughts and images. Were you able to change the bull into the dove? If so, how close did he come before you did? For most people, the bull comes within a few feet before they are able to make the change.

What does it mean when we allow the bull to get right up in our faces, or even let it attack us? I use the words *allow* and *let* because we are the ones who have created these images; we are in control of them. However, for most of us, the opposite seems to be true; they seem to be controlling us. We need to realize that we do not have to hold negative images in our minds, or continue to think and feel in ways that are not good for us. We never have to be victims of any thoughts and images that pop up automati-cally. We can manipulate them so that they do not continue to cause us harm.

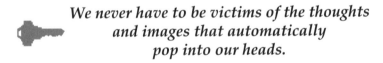

*We never have to be victims of the thoughts and images that automatically pop into our heads.*

With replacement, what you are doing is taking any nega-tive image, like the bull, and turning it into one that is positive (for example, a dove). This is within your control. You always have the ability to focus on something pleasant. Practice focusing on the good things, past and present. The better you get at it, the less stress you'll experience.

You may want to try the bull exercise again and deliberately take more control this time. Change the bull into the dove before he comes near you, maybe as soon as you see him standing there. A woman in one of my workshops said that the bull did indeed attack her in her visualization. She had to do this exercise three times before she could change the bull into the dove. She finally shouted with excitement, "I did it! I did it!" The entire class cheered for her. It was a great moment of insight as she discovered the power of her own mind.

> EXERCISE: **Face-to-Face Confrontation (Replacement).** After reading this paragraph, close your eyes and recall a face-to-face confrontation you have had with someone. Imagine that you are looking into the other person's eyes; recall it just the way it happened. Then change the negative image into one that is positive. Replace the face of that person who is causing you stress with the face of someone you love. If you are able to do this successfully, your body will respond in much more beneficial ways.
>
> Another element you might want to add to this imagery is to change the location where the scene takes place; put yourself in a neutral or peaceful setting instead. You will notice positive changes in your body immediately; you will begin to feel better. You can apply this technique of re-placement for images of the past, present, and future.

## Dissociation

We can use dissociation for stress relief by deliberately switching from the associative perspective and seeing an image or event as an observer rather than as an active participant. Use this technique to manipulate negative images and to feel better. (For more discussion on this, refer back to the section on perspective awareness in Chapter 10.)

> EXERCISE: **Face-to-Face Confrontation (Dissociation).** Use your image from the previous exercise. In a moment, close your eyes and imagine yourself in that scene as the partici-pant, looking into the eyes of the other person (associat-ing). Then change the perspective so that you can experi-ence it dissociatively; Watch the scene from a distance as if you are an objective outsider. Become aware of the changes in your body's response. Typically you will not feel threat-ened in the same way. To enhance this process, once you

have dissociated, practice moving the scene farther from you in a physical sense. Push the scene away or move back in your mind so that the image is barely visible. Again, you are neutralizing the negative effects of stress by using your mind.

### Manipulating Images in the Past, Present, and Future

**The Past.** Most of us recall memories from an associative perspective, exactly as we experienced them the first time. Suppose there is a memory of an unhappy moment or situation that causes you to feel stressed whenever you recall it. With each recollection, your body re-experiences the same negative emotions.

The next time that memory starts to surface either replace that thought with one that is more pleasant, or use your mind to see that image from a dissociative perspective (as you did in the previous exercise). By switching from the participant to the observer, you will not feel the same intensity that you would if you were associating. You could imagine that you are watching yourself on a stage, as if you were in a play. By doing this, you not only neutralize the negative effects of the stressful situation, but also, you are taking more control over your mental process.

 *Dwelling on stressful events of the past can cause us more harm in the long run than the original source of that stress.*

**The Present.** It may be difficult to use replacement and dissociation to reduce stress that is generated in the present moment. If, for example, you're conducting a meeting, you need to be alert and present in the moment. Switching perspectives would obviously not be appropriate in that type of circumstance. If you must keep your eyes open, positive self-talk and deep breathing are your best bets to reduce stress.

If you are able to close your eyes in the middle of a situation, it will be much easier to mentally manipulate the current scene. The following is an exercise that will help you practice changing perspectives in the middle of a stressful situation, one in which you can refocus your mind.

EXERCISE: **At the Dentist (Dissociation).** Close your eyes, take a full, deep breath, and see yourself sitting in a dentist's chair from across the room. Watch from a distance as the dentist works on your teeth. Then switch perspectives and imagine that you are sitting in the chair, feeling the chair under you, and seeing the dentist standing beside your chair. You can see the needle; you know you are about to get a few shots. You start to feel a little bit nervous. When you begin to experience that nervousness in your body, change your perspective. Dissociate yourself from that chair. Stand across the room again as an observer. Continue to focus on this perspective as long as you need to. This process helps to remove much of the stress from that potentially stressful situation.

If you have difficulty dissociating or just need a little help, look at some photographs of yourself or watch yourself on a video. It will give you handy reference points when you need to switch perspectives to feel better. Put your mind to work to help yourself in all kinds of current situations, any time you need to relieve stress. Remember to practice; then, when the time comes, you'll be prepared.

**The Future.** What do you usually do when you worry or are afraid of something? You probably say, "What if . . . ?" and then imagine a negative or fearful situation that might occur. You probably then step into that scene in your mind as if it were actually happening (association). Your imagination can be very vivid as you conjure up the worst possible situations. Does this sound familiar? Becoming the observer (dissociation) of a possible future situation will help distance you from the actual feelings you might normally have. Looking at the scene as an objective third party helps you to be more rational and less emotional in your thinking. An even better idea is to replace the negative scene with one that is exactly how you would like the future to be.

EXERCISE: **"What if?" (Replacement and Dissociation).** Think of a situation that causes you to worry or be fearful. Dissociating may help you feel better, so close your eyes and try that; see how it works for you. Next, replace the negative situation with one that you choose. Ask yourself, "How do I want to experience this?" Then, in your mind, create the future the way you want it to be.

## Practice Linking the Good with the Bad and Ugly

If a particularly disturbing image continues to appear, the more you practice switching perspectives, the easier it will become. As the disturbing image makes its presence known to you, the second image (the positive one where you dissociate) becomes linked automatically. Even if you initially think of the negative image, you will see that the other one comes in right behind it. You are creating a new pattern of thinking and, thus, changing the way you feel. Allow the first to pass quickly, then accept the second one as your preference.

Here is an example of how switching perspectives from associative to dissociative helped me ease my mind and body after a disturbing event. A speeding car hit my son's cat, Jack. We found Jack in the street; he was already dead. Jack was part of our family, and it was devastating to see him lying there. We covered him with a towel. We were very upset not only because we lost Jack, but also because we had such a horrible last image of him in our minds. As I grieved that night, the terrible image kept reappearing in my mind.

I knew I had to put my mind to work. I sat quietly, closed my eyes and began to relax. Then I saw the scene just as I had originally experienced it: right there up close, next to my son, stooping down over Jack. I switched perspectives and placed myself farther down the street, watching my son and me with Jack. I became a bystander, an observer, of my actual experience. (Sometimes our minds automatically switch back to the associative perspective, so repetition may be necessary until you gain more control.)

Even from a distance, I was still sad to see him that way; but can you understand how it decreased my emotional involvement in the scene? It was much less painful to watch than to participate. This image made it much easier for me to cope with his death. Over the next few days, whenever the horrible mental image appeared, I immediately replaced it with the new one. I took a few more moments to recall happy memories of us playing with Jack, holding him in my lap, laughing, and enjoying him. When I changed the thoughts and images in my mind, I could literally feel the difference in my body. Time heals wounded hearts, but wouldn't you prefer to do it as quickly as possible?

By the way, my son found another cat at the humane society, coincidentally named Jack, that he promptly adopted.

You can change your experience of sad or painful events by putting your mind to work for your advantage. Link the good with the bad and ugly, if that's what you need to help yourself feel better.

## Stress and Breathing

When you are in a stressful situation, you typically breathe with only the top one-third to one-half of your lungs. If your diaphragm is not doing the work of breathing, what do you think is? Your neck, upper chest, and back muscles! This causes undue strain, tension, and spasms. Notice your breathing pattern the next time you feel stressed. If you become aware that your breathing is rapid and shallow, inhale deeply from the bottom of your lungs, and hold your breath a few seconds before exhaling slowly.

By taking a few belly breaths, you bring in more oxygen to your brain. This helps you to feel not only more alert and focused, but also more calm and in control—just the way you need to feel when you're under stress.

Also, by taking in more oxygen, your heart doesn't have to work so hard, bringing your heart rate and blood pressure down. The medical research journal *Hypertension* reports that just two ten-minute sessions a day of slow, deep breathing can lower blood pressure dramatically.

*Belly breaths positively affect your heart rate, blood pressure, and anxiety level.*

## Plan for Stress

You can sometimes plan ahead for stress. If you know that you will be in a stressful situation, or think you might be, wear comfortable clothing, something loose-fitting around your waist and chest. It's much easier to breathe deeply when the expansion of your lungs is not restricted. Give your body a chance to work for you. The simple act of taking control over your breathing allows you to take more physical and emotional control and provides extraordinary benefits. Most people don't breathe deeply simply because they don't understand how important it is.

A side note: If you are a smoker, think about how many deep breaths you take with just one cigarette. You inhale slowly and deeply, and you feel more relaxed, not because of what is inside the cigarette or the chemicals produced (nicotine is a stimulant), but because of the deep breaths you're taking! Smokers associate the feeling of being more relaxed with smoking. This creates a mental link between cigarettes and relaxation. Whenever a smoker needs to feel relaxed, he or she gets out the cigarette that has become a "friend" and puffs away. Isn't it ironic that what makes you feel better is really killing you? Take deep breaths throughout the day without the cigarettes—you'll likely feel more calm and in control, and it should be much easier to stop smoking.

In this chapter, you've learned about several different stress reduction strategies to help you feel better, both physically and emotionally. The next chapter continues with our focus on managing stress, as we look at living joyfully.

# 13

# *Discovering Joy*

*Being, not doing, is my first joy.*

—THEODORE ROETHKE

Do you know one of the best ways to help you deal with stress and stay healthy, physically and emotionally? It is to lighten up and learn to live joyfully! To feel better, create joy on purpose. Since everlasting happiness is a myth, we must focus on moments instead of forever. Moments in the present—that's all we really have, and it's up to us as to how we fill those precious pieces of time.

## Imagining Joy to Relieve Stress

When you are under a lot of pressure and feel stressed, take time out to use your imagination. Close your eyes, breathe deeply, then relive your best moments. Go back to a special vacation in your mind; daydream about a place you want to go or something you hope to do. Re-experience an uplifting, joyful moment. Make it as real as possible in your mind by using your senses; feel the joy emotionally and physically.

To intensify happy feelings, make sure you are using the associative perspective, either with past or future scenes. Be mindful of the joy in each present moment so you will have wonderful memories to experience again and again. Remember that your brain and subconscious cannot tell the difference between a real event and one that you vividly imagine.

When life gets hectic, it's difficult to stop and smell the roses; but you can still smell them while you run through life if you carry them with you in your mind. If nothing else, when you are hurrying through your day, breathe deeply and imagine the roses' rich fragrance. You'll catch yourself smiling.

Learning to create moments of joy for ourselves is extraordinary because it can help change the way we think and feel. We can spend our time and energy generating thoughts and images that help us experience more peace of mind. When we do, we experience less stress. The more stress we feel, the more joy we need to bring into our lives. It is especially important at these times that we force ourselves to feel joyful, even when we are not in the mood to be happy. This is what we need; this is what's good for us. Take care of yourself and experience more joy; escape to serenity for a change.

EXERCISE: **Escape to Serenity at the Beach.** Read this paragraph, then close your eyes for a few minutes and imagine walking along the shore at the beach (if you enjoy being at the ocean). Sense the wet sand under your bare feet. Feel the refreshing water splash on your feet and lower legs. Listen to the sea gulls and the sound of the ocean waves— notice how beautiful the deep blue water is. Feel the warmth of the sun on your shoulders and the cool, ocean breeze blowing gently across your face. Take a full deep breath, breathing in the salt air; you can almost taste it. Notice how calm, content, and carefree you feel. Then let your eyes open.

As you use your imagination, your senses are feeding information to your brain, which is registering that you *are* on the beach. What an inexpensive getaway! Your body starts producing endorphins, natural chemicals that make you feel better physically and psychologically.

 *Endorphins are the body's natural chemicals that act as painkillers and mood boosters.*

## Experiencing Joy in Reality

Not only can we create more joy in our imaginations, but we can also create more joy in reality. There is no reason we must wait for exhilaration to come to us through our circumstances; we can make it happen for ourselves. One thing we can do is to become more aware and appreciate some of the wonderfully uplifting things in our surroundings. Don't just *look* at things; see what is before you in all its luminous and fleeting grandeur. Develop an "Oh, wow!" attitude; experience moments of surprise and delight.

### Think about Nature

The sky, clouds, breezes, water, trees, flowers, animals, mountains, shores, plains, rain, snowflakes, sunshine, and rainbows—all of nature's splendor, always there for our pleasure. Perhaps the reason we have so many extraordinary natural spectacles is to uplift our weary hearts. Nature reminds us that we are part of something much larger than ourselves, and that there is order in the universe and a purpose for everything. It instills in us faith and hope. (Have you ever noticed that morning glories reach toward the sun even when it's raining?) When we are truly in touch with nature, we sense a connection to everything around us and beyond; that is an extraordinary experience! If you can learn to appreciate and respect nature, you can learn to appreciate and respect yourself. Allow the breathtaking beauty of nature to help you escape from your troubles for a while. In doing so, you will not only be better able to cope with what comes your way, you will also discover how to live more joyfully.

I have found many ways to create my own joy. One way is to view nature up close. I use several magnifying glasses (the small ones jewelers use are especially good). Have you ever seen the inside of a tiny, white lily-of-the-valley flower or a fuzzy-looking fern frond just barely beginning to unfold? Have you noticed how early morning dewdrops on rosebush leaves form a perfect pattern around the pointed edges? Taking photographs of these natural spectacles is another way to focus on joy. There is a world of wonder in things that are not easily visible to the naked eye. Look for, and discover, a whole new world right at your feet.

## Happy Links to the Past

Surround yourself with things that give you comfort and peace, things that help you remember wonderful memories: framed photographs, books, keepsakes, and cherished items. Fill the air with your favorite scents (essential oils and candles). Put flowers where you can enjoy them. A gardenia sits next to me today; it reminds me of the bouquets I gave my first grade teacher. Yesterday, roses and honeysuckle brought a sweet remembrance of my grandmother.

## Music

Each morning I awaken to the sounds of "The Joy of Life," a song by the jazz musician Kenny G. It starts off gently and brings to mind images of the rising sun. What a great way to start a new day! Play your favorite music, calm and soothing, or energizing and uplifting; sing or hum along. The fast-paced music of Yanni, the Greek composer and musician, or Enya's "Caribbean Blue" will definitely lift your spirits! No sad songs are allowed! The idea is to feel better, not worse. Use your head!

## Creating Rainbows

A fun thing to do that will brighten your life is to create your own rainbows (real ones). One way is to turn your back to the sun and spray a mist of water in front of you. Sometimes you can see double rainbows. You can also hang crystals in your windows and invite the sun to cast splashes of brilliant colors all around you. As I sit typing at my computer, purple and blue lights stretch across my fingers and catch my attention—what an unexpected delight! "Oh, wow!"

## Laughter

As children we laughed hundreds of times a day, but for most of us, as we grow older, the laughter tapers off, doesn't it? Laugh and make life fun. Don't sit back and wait for it to happen to you. Take more control by giving yourself permission to feel lighthearted and more carefree, even if just for a little while each day. Watch funny movies and stage plays. Be more childlike. Blow bubbles. Hum, sing songs, and whistle; play music or beat on drums. Dance, run, and play! When was the last time you skipped? Dare yourself to skip today!

The next time you're hurrying somewhere in a car and have to stop to wait for a long train to pass, instead of sitting there feeling stressed, do what I do: Open the windows and blow bubbles. I keep a plastic bubble tumbler handy. When you're blowing bubbles, you immediately change the way you feel—not to mention helping others to lighten up, too. So what if they think you're crazy. You're the one who is in control—don't worry so much about what other people think.

Accept what you cannot change (how long the train will delay you), and change what you can (your attitude). Flow through life instead of struggling unnecessarily. Think about it: When you are experiencing happiness, even if only for a few moments, you aren't feeling any negative emotions. Instead, you're not only relieving stress and promoting wellness, you are also living more successfully. Isn't that what you want?

## When Was the Last Time You Experienced Joy?

Ask yourself, "When was the last time I experienced joy?" Your answer to this question is important feedback on how fully you are living your life. For some people it has been years, and for others months, weeks, or days. Hopefully, it's only been hours or minutes. Next, ask yourself "How often do I want to experience joy?"

Most of us want and need to have some kind of joy in our lives every single day. If it's been a while since you felt joyous, I encourage you to redefine your meaning of joy to include moments of happiness, however short-lived they may be. Every day is a new opportunity to create joy in your life—to change the way you think, how you feel and what you do. Today, listen for birds singing in distant trees or notice the tiny veins in a leaf. Hum a happy tune, even if you don't feel like it. Think of something funny and let yourself laugh. Especially when you are sad or have a lot of stress in your life, you need to create joy for yourself as often as you can. Lift yourself up!

## Creating Joy Beyond Words

When we feel joyful, we have a natural tendency to use words, out loud or silently, to describe the event. When we finish our description, we have an opportunity to go beyond that point, and expand and lengthen our experiences, without using thoughts and words.

What do I mean by this? Our moments of joy become longer lasting and more profound when we no longer have a need to explain our experiences, only to be aware of them. This is *pure awareness;* it is a sensation or feeling that becomes indescribable. We usually have a sense of being connected with whatever it is that holds our attention. During these moments, we experience absolute joy and peace.

Think about a time when you may have looked lovingly at a sleeping baby. Maybe you remember noticing its beautiful face. You may have whispered softly, "You are so sweet and precious, and I love you." When you stopped using words to describe the baby and your feelings, and just stared, smiling, the experience became a moment of pure awareness. That moment of true connection was filled not only with joy and peace, but also love. This is joy beyond words. First become aware of this kind of experience, then practice expanding these moments; you will find that your life naturally becomes more joyful.

An old Chinese proverb says, "May your way of life be calm and serene, and may you always have great enjoyment in living." Notice that it doesn't say, "May *your life* be calm and serene . . ." It says, "May your *way of life* be calm and serene . . ." Having a sense of control over *how* you experience life is the best way to live joyfully and successfully.

# 14

# *Wellness*

*Our emotions and words let the body know what
we expect of it, and by visualizing certain changes
we can help the body bring them about.*

—Bernie Siegel, M.D.

**W**ellness is one of my favorite topics for presentations to
groups. I gain a tremendous amount of satisfaction in
helping individuals understand how they can maintain or enhance their own wellness. Illness is what caused me to reevaluate
how I was living my life. It helped me prioritize what was really
important and understand my purpose. As a speaker, I am passionate about sharing my life-changing experience with my audiences so that I might inspire others to believe in themselves and
their power to heal their own lives.

 *Peace of mind is the ultimate
extraordinary accomplishment.*

# Modern Science and Ancient Wisdom

For centuries, people in India and the Far Eastern countries like China and Japan believed in, and practiced using, the healing powers of the mind. With modern Western science, much of the belief in our natural abilities went by the wayside; however, that is beginning to change. We will enhance the future of medicine by drawing from the best of both worlds—modern science and ancient wisdom.

We have long heard that the ancient practice of meditation is beneficial to health. What is meditation? Basically, it is deep relaxation of the mind and body. Generally, visualization, if used at all, is for the specific purpose of relaxation and focusing awareness. The word *meditate* can be traced to the Latin word *mederi* that means "to remedy, to heal." Research suggests that meditation does just that.

Some doctors prescribe meditation to neutralize the negative effects of stress. Dr. Herbert Benson of Harvard Medical School, is the president and founder of The Mind/Body Medical Institute. He recommends meditation to soothe the turmoil the body feels under stress. Dr. Joan Borysenko, author of *Minding the Body, Mending the Mind,* says, "We are entering a new level in the scientific understanding of mechanisms by which faith, belief and imagination can actually unlock the mysteries of healing."

Ongoing scientific research is proving that the powers of the mind are real and can help physical conditions such as migraines, heart disease, and even cancer. Not only has Harvard Medical School established The Mind/Body Medical Institute, there is also the Office for the Study of Unconventional Medical Practices at the National Institutes of Health. The power of the mind has become an accepted part of the healing process. In spite of strides made through research, a good part of the medical community in the United States has been slow to accept the latest findings.

## Mind Over Matter: The Placebo Effect

In scientific studies of medical treatments, often one group of patients is given the actual medicine, while the other group receives a placebo—an inactive substance with no medicinal effects (often a sugar pill). The *placebo effect* refers to the scientific finding that when people have been told that they are receiving potent drugs, but have actually been given placebos (sugar pills), many people produce not only the same therapeutic outcome of using the actual drug, but the side effects as well. The belief that their bodies will react a certain way is at least as powerful as the drugs themselves. Patients who believe they will get better are more likely to recover.

## Destroying or Nurturing the Body?

Think about how incredibly miraculous the human body is. Millions of cells perform more complicated jobs than most of us can imagine. Systems work together perfectly, all without our conscious awareness. It is a billion-dollar machine, but we don't seem to treat it that way, do we? We abuse our bodies in almost every way: too much of the wrong kinds of foods, not enough healthy foods, lack of exercise, use of tobacco and drugs, excessive alcohol consumption, and lack of rest and sleep. Taking care of ourselves physically is as important as nurturing ourselves mentally and emotionally. If we develop a deep respect and love for ourselves, we can develop that same respect for our bodies. We can learn to appreciate the extraordinary human machine of life.

*The body is a miraculous billion-dollar machine. Take care of it!*

Andrew Weil, M.D. provides useful information on developing a healthy lifestyle in his excellent books, *Eight Weeks to Optimum Health* and *Spontaneous Healing*. Dr. Weil, a proponent of a synthesis of conventional and alternative medical treatments, helps us understand more about the interaction of mind and body and how we can tap into the natural resources within ourselves.

To create vibrant health, Christiane Northrup, M.D., author of *Women's Bodies, Women's Minds* and *Women's Bodies, Women's*

*Choices*, suggests that we need "... laughter, sunshine and natural light, nutritious food, clean air and water, a fulfilling sex life, uplifting relationships, outdoor exercise, satisfying living and working environment, natural sleep and relaxation, inspiring music and rhythmical dance."

It's interesting to know that cells of the immune system manufacture the same chemicals as your brain does when it thinks. This helps us understand what today's medical pioneers like Deepak Chopra, author and physician from India, are saying: that the mind is literally in every cell within the body. Given this information, we can see how our thoughts could either be creating or destroying healthy tissue. We know that the mind and body are intertwined; it makes perfect sense to fill our minds with positive thoughts and images, and create uplifting sensations and feelings. This can have very positive effects on our bodies. Enhancing and maintaining wellness can certainly be described as extraordinary accomplishments.

## Visualizing Radiant Health

We can put our minds to work to enhance our well-being if we have any type of physical problem: anything from a minor, temporary ailment such as a sore throat, to a life-threatening illness like cancer or heart disease. We can also use our minds when we are well to focus on comfort, fitness, and remaining in good health.

According to *The New England Journal of Medicine*, visualization is one of the most frequently used forms of alternative healing. Meditation, deep relaxation, and visualization can be considered complementary therapies and are almost always used in conjunction with traditional medical treatments. In the book *Remarkable Recovery* by Caryle Hirshberg and Marc Ian Barasch, we find documentation of individuals making the most of their extraordinary powers within, enabling them to conquer what medicine tells us is unconquerable.

We know that our bodies follow our thoughts and images. We can mentally guide our physical bodies to follow positive thoughts and images. Using creative imagery designed for our specific needs encourages our minds and bodies to work together in harmony. Learning as much as we can about the biological process we want to affect may help to create ideal images for use in visualization. The process can simply be to sense the body as radiantly healthy, creating the ideal situation, with the body working perfectly.

According to research by the Cleveland Clinic Foundation, as quoted in the January, 1998 issue of *Self* magazine, "Before, during or after surgery, listening to tapes that combine soothing music, descriptions of relaxing places and messages about the body's healing powers can speed recovery." Patients who listened to guided imagery programs ". . . were one-third less anxious, needed half as much pain medication and had shorter hospital stays and fewer complications than nonlisteners."

When our eyes are closed and we are focusing inwardly, one of the most important channels for mind-body communication becomes available. Dr. Andrew Weil recommends, "Try using visualizations to speed up the healing of wounds, sore throats, and other common ailments. Then if you ever have to mobilize your healing resources to manage a serious illness, you will have a good head start."

> *Enhance and maintain wellness by filling your mind with positive thoughts and images, and inviting your body to follow along.*

EXERCISE: **Tuning into the Body.** Close your eyes, take a few deep breaths (you know the routine), and become aware of your heart beating. Feel it pumping the blood, listen to the sounds, sense your pulse in different areas, and visualize your blood flowing through your arteries and veins. Feel the warmth of the circulating fluid. See your blood vessels as normal, open, and clear.

Practice receptive imagery; move your awareness to different parts of your body and become aware of any sensations and feelings as you go along. Be open to thoughts and images that seem to pop into your mind. These can be helpful in creating the concepts and images that have meaning for you.

Next, move your awareness to any area of your body needing special attention. Use your mind to actively imagine energy, such as heat or light, surrounding and penetrating the area. In whatever way is easy and natural for you, see it as normal and healthy, just the way you want it to be.

# Cancer

Research by Stephanie Simonton, Ph.D., director of the Behavioral Medicine Program for the University of Arkansas for Medical Sciences, and co-author of *Getting Well Again*, tells us that with the cancer patients studied, there was a significant correlation between immune system enhancement and the frequency of relaxation and visualization practice. "These results suggest that even after the immunosuppressive effects of radiation therapy, cancer patients appear capable of enhancing their immune competence via psychological techniques."

In other studies, patients with cancer that had spread to other parts of their bodies were taught to practice imagery. Positive changes were found in several components of their immune systems. The degree of improvement was directly associated with the frequency and quality of the imagery.

# Pain

Individuals experiencing chronic pain, for whom I have created personalized programs, say they're able to find relief for several hours after listening to the guided imagery which focuses on their specific needs. Each time they practice deep relaxation and creative visualization, they are producing more endorphins, and enhancing wellness, comfort, and peace of mind.

Pain can also be relieved through the use of replacement and dissociation. (Refer back to Chapter 12.)

# Sleep Difficulties

When we don't get enough sleep, stress hormone levels go up and those related to immune functioning go down. There is also concern that lack of sleep can accelerate the aging process. Sufficient sleep provides us with needed rest for energy, clear thinking, and problem solving. Deep sleep replenishes chemicals in the brain called *neurotransmitters*. They send messages from one nerve cell to another and are depleted during our waking hours. Without these neurotransmitters we could not think, breathe, or move. Researchers believe that the replenishment of these chemicals, which occurs during rapid eye movement (REM) sleep, is the physiological basis for our saying that we feel refreshed and energized after a good night's sleep.

When it's time to sleep, do you ever lie in bed in the darkened room and feel wide awake? Your body may be tired, but your mind is racing from one thought to another. Perhaps you dwell on one or two negative thoughts that cause you distress. You think, "I'll never get to sleep like this."

You may finally fall asleep, then wake up a few hours later. Maybe you wake up and you still have two hours before your alarm will go off. You lie there trying to force yourself to go back to sleep. These are typical occurrences experienced by millions of people every day.

Stress is related to our sleep patterns. The more stress we feel, the less sleep we experience; and the less sleep we get, the more we feel stressed. Using stress reduction strategies can help us get the rest we need. The better we sleep, the more productive we are in our waking hours; we feel more energetic, alert, and are geared for peak performance.

There are simple techniques you can use to help you fall asleep more easily. One way is to focus on relaxing the tension in your muscles. Another way is to "put your troubles in bubbles" (see Chapter 7). You could simply imagine slowly pushing aside any distracting thoughts. You may want to visualize relaxing in a special place where your mind is carefree.

# Believe that You Deserve to Be Healthy

Our beliefs about ourselves are closely linked to our health. If we believe in our hearts that we are unworthy, if we have a subconscious need to punish ourselves for past mistakes, can you understand how that impacts the way we treat ourselves? A woman whom I had never met called me to ask if I could help her figure out why she had been unsuccessful in giving up cigarettes. She had tried several times to quit her three-pack-a-day habit. I asked her questions about her life. She told me that she was a recovering alcoholic and that she felt terribly guilty for the ways she had treated her children when they were growing up. She said this was something that she focused on every single day. Could it be that she somehow subconsciously, unintentionally, pro-grammed herself to feel that she deserved to be punished? If that were the case, smoking cigarettes, which made her sick, was a way to accomplish that.

# Unintentional Programming

We move in the direction of our dominant thoughts (or subconscious programs), even if we are unaware of how they are linked to our behaviors.

We sometimes unintentionally program our minds to create illnesses. We might think to ourselves, "My parent had cancer at age 50, so I probably will, too." We know that our bodies follow our thoughts.

A story my father told me helps to explain this concept. My grandfather died when he was 49 years old and my father was eleven. In a child's mind 49 seems fairly old. After being told of his death, my father held his dog and cried. In his deeply emotional state, he said, "I don't want to die; I want to live to be as old as my dad." This statement in essence programmed his subconscious mind with a set of instructions as to what he wanted at that time: to live to be 49 years old.

When my father was in his mid-forties, although he could not explain why, he said he had a sense that he would not be around much longer. When he decided to take out more life insurance for his family, he had to have several medical tests run. The tests revealed that his heart was in such bad shape that he could have dropped dead at any time. This alarming news caused him to begin searching for answers about life and death. He looked deeply within himself and asked, "Why am I near death?" What came to him in his mind was a moment back in time as that 11-year-old boy; he heard himself speaking to his dog on the day his father passed away. The literal meaning of those words became very clear. He realized that he had unintentionally programmed his body to give out at 49 years of age.

He learned how to use his mind to reprogram the outdated set of instructions. It was time to live! I am happy to say that my father recently celebrated his 70th birthday. Way to go, Dad!

## How Long Do You Want to Live?

If I asked you how long you wanted to live, what would say? When I ask this question in workshops, the typical answer is around 75 years. Years ago I imagined myself sitting quietly in my rocker at 80, looking through my photograph albums. Now that I have changed my mind, I prefer to see myself living my golden years walking along the beach, taking more photographs—out and about, actively living life to the fullest. Right now I am shooting for somewhere around 100, but that may be subject to change—upward of course! When I mention this to others, they usually ask, "Why would you want to live that long?" My response: "I love living!"

 *No matter how long we live,*
*we must learn to live deeply and joyfully.*

# Are There Simple Answers for Illness?

There are no simple answers when we ask, "Why did I get sick?" Dr. Andrew Weil, during a television interview, discussed the link between the mind and body. He suggested that we ". . . look at what is going on in our lives. What emotional pains could we be suppressing in our heads that are being transferred in physical ways?" This is not to say that we cause our illnesses; but, if the possibility exists that our emotions contribute in any way, isn't it worth looking into? The next chapter will be helpful in taking a closer look at this subject.

Maybe all we can do is learn from what happens to us and make the very best use of our time to enhance the quality of our lives. When we have an illness, we can choose to give up or do everything we can to help ourselves. We can take an active role in our well-being. Bernie S. Siegel, M.D., author of *Love, Medicine & Miracles* and *Peace, Love & Healing*, and the man who helped renew my life, suggests that, although we may not be in complete control of the final outcome of what happens to our physical bodies, we can control our attitudes, how we treat ourselves, and what we bring into our lives.

> *You must believe that you deserve to take good care of yourself and that you deserve to be healthy.*

If these are not your beliefs, you need to get to work immediately to change them. Only then will you be open to the idea of wellness; only then will you be able to heal your life.

# 15

# *Getting Rid of the Excess Baggage*

*The mind is its own place, and in itself, can make heaven of hell or a hell of heaven.*

—John Milton

We tend to carry with us on our journey, negative emotions from the past (and sometimes future expectations). This "excess baggage" is filled with feelings that we don't need.

Why do we do this? Maybe it's just a habit, something to which we are accustomed. It is very uncomfortable for us to haul around these heavy burdens, but we do it anyway. We may be afraid to let go of something that has become an integral part of who we are. We are full of regrets. We know how to feel angry, hurt, and guilty; we are used to feeling afraid and worrying. We don't know what it feels like to be free of this negative energy. Negative feelings weigh us down and keep us from living our lives fully and freely. Focusing on them wastes time and robs us of valuable energy. This can take an enormous toll on our health and enjoyment of life. When we allow ourselves to let go of these harmful emotions, there is more room in our hearts for peace, joy, and love.

## Examining Negative Emotions

One thing you can do to help yourself is to examine the following list of negative emotions to see what you are carrying as excess baggage. In the past few days, weeks, or months have you experienced any of the following? Check the appropriate spaces.

| | |
|---|---|
| ___ Anger | ___ Jealousy |
| ___ Boredom | ___ Laziness |
| ___ Discouragement | ___ Nervousness |
| ___ Fear | ___ Panic |
| ___ Frustration | ___ Rage |
| ___ Grief | ___ Regret |
| ___ Guilt | ___ Resentment |
| ___ Hatred | ___ Sadness |
| ___ Hopelessness | ___ Worry |
| ___ Hostility | ___ Other _____ |
| ___ Irritation | _____ |

Think about the emotions you checked. When you experienced these emotions, was it in response to situations that had just happened, or have these emotions been with you for a long time? If needed, go deeper within yourself to identify the underlying sources of these feelings.

All of us, at one time or another, experience some of these; none are good for us if we continue to hold on to them. Do they interfere with your living joyfully and successfully? Do they keep you awake at night? Do you wake up with a feeling of having a heavy weight on your chest? (Your body is simply following your thoughts.) Where are you depleting your resources?

Holding onto negative emotions only hurts us; it's like acid eating away at our minds and bodies. It makes life much more difficult than it has to be. Do you want those feelings to be part of your life? If you want to make this journey easier and more enjoyable, you need to get rid of them!

We have already discussed two ways that can be used to deal with many negative emotions: replacement and dissociation. (Refer back to Chapter 12.)

### Anger, Guilt, and Regret

Of all of the emotions in the list on the previous page, anger, guilt, and regret are among the most common. Some of this negative energy is directed at others because of what they have done to us, or for the hurtful things they have said. Understand and remember that what others do and say is a reflection of who *they* are, and that has nothing to do with you. Substitute anger with indifference; you will find that your enemies no longer seem to matter.

Many times we direct some of the anger inward. We hold ourselves responsible for what we call mistakes. We hold onto guilt as if we deserve to be punished forever. Do you remember the guilt-ridden smoker? We may think that we are unworthy of happiness. We have regrets about what we did, as well as what we failed to do; we feel we should have done things differently. Would anyone blame a mother whose son was killed in car accident because she said, "Yes" when asked if he could go out with his friends? We think, "If only I had . . ." or "If only I hadn't . . ." We beat ourselves up emotionally, sometimes for the rest of our lives. We carry around that excess baggage from the past and experience life as a tremendous struggle.

*Two useful contributions of the past:*
*lessons that will help us now*
*and in the future,*
*and happy times to remember.*

### Fear and Worry

Fear is anxiety caused by real or possible danger or pain. Our fearful thoughts, feelings, and behaviors are reasonable when certain harm might befall us. However, most of our fears are unfounded. We use our imaginations to project learned fear into future events (worry); this is definitely not using our minds effectively.

Instead of thinking about how terrible fear is, think how fear can help us. We would never become courageous without experiencing fear. We build courage and self-confidence every time we force ourselves to do something that we really want to do even though we may feel afraid.

We need to go beyond our comfort zone and push ourselves to meet challenges. The problem for many of us is that we run from those things that make us afraid instead of tapping into our inner strength and facing them. Henry Ford said, "One of the great discoveries a man makes, one of his great surprises is to find he can do what he was afraid he couldn't do." Discover your courage as you try new ways of thinking and behaving. In this process you become more of the kind of person you want to be.

# Letting Go

In order to let go of our excess baggage we must first become aware of the negative emotions that fill our hearts. Next, we need to give ourselves permission to let go of these harmful feelings; then we can use our minds to destroy them, or leave them in the past where they belong.

## Letting Go through Guided Imagery

We can use our creative imaginations to give our inner minds a new set of instructions about what we want and need to carry with us into the future. Remember that a picture is worth at least a thousand words, especially to our subconscious. This mental process may take anywhere from only a few minutes one time, to once a day for several weeks, until the subconscious "gets the picture."

In some of my work with individuals, we go through the mental process of releasing negative emotions that no longer serve any useful purpose with guided imagery. Together we create the needed concepts and images to inform their subconscious minds of what they want and need for the present and future. Processing (or transforming) negativity is an essential step toward achieving peace of mind. I often use this as a preliminary step in the process of developing personalized programs.

**Forgiveness**

Part of the process of releasing negative feelings from the past involves forgiveness. If you want to change the way you feel and experience life more successfully, consider forgiving yourself and others. It may not be easy, but it is always worth the effort. Parents, relatives, friends, lovers, co-workers, all the people in your life have done their best, even if it doesn't seem that way. They may have made many mistakes, and they may continue to behave in the same old ways. Maybe they knew what they were doing was wrong, but they were obviously unable to make better decisions, to be better persons. They either were incapable of doing things differently, or they just didn't know how. It's important to understand that when people are mean, spiteful, and critical of others, it usually indicates that they are unhappy inside; they want everyone around them to feel just as miserable as they do. This is sad, isn't it?

Sometimes just the thought of someone who has hurt you causes you to feel sad or angry. Your body physically responds to this thought and affects you in a variety of negative ways. Isn't it time you let go of the negative energy that keeps you bound to those who have caused you pain? When you forgive others, know that you are not doing it for them, but for yourself.

> *Forgiveness is an act of courage;*
> *be courageous.*

Isn't it time to forgive yourself? Try thinking this way: You came into this world knowing nothing. Everything you have learned has been accomplished at the price of literally thousands of mistakes. You fell hundreds of times before you walked. You gradually learned how to ride a bike, drive a car, and how to find your way in a new city. You cannot expect to know something until you learn it; expect to make mistakes! This learning process goes on your entire life, and so do the mistakes. This only means that you are living your life, doing things, and moving forward. Accept and love yourself, mistakes and all. Remember that you are doing your best; you always have and you always will. Forgive yourself for not being perfect and accept your human-ness.

In a quiet moment, affirm to yourself an understanding and acceptance of the idea that others have done the best they could at the time under the circumstances. Creating this belief will help you to feel empathy and compassion for those who have hurt you. It will allow you to let go of the heavy burden of guilt and regret; you can then more easily feel empathy and compassion for your-self. See your mistakes as stepping stones on your way to becoming more of the kind of person you want to be. The author James Joyce said, "A man of genius makes no mistakes. His errors are the portals of discovery."

    *Discover, learn, and move forward.*

## Editing and Creating Our Past

You cannot change the reality of actual events of the past; however—please pay attention because this is important—*you can change the way you feel about them.* Remember, the realities of your experiences are stored in your subconscious mind. So how can you change the way you feel about your experiences? Give your subconscious mind (the feeling part) new and different pieces of information about an event that actually happened or one that you wish had occurred. In this way you create a new "memory" for your subconscious to store as a reality. Consciously, you are aware that it didn't really happen, but somehow you feel as though it did. Let me share with you some examples so this will become more clear.

## A Triathlete Is Born

Swimming in a pool with water waist-high was easy enough for 45-year-old Bill, but with his fear of deep, open water, finishing a triathlon was next to impossible. He had to pull out of his first event because he was unable to complete the swim portion. Bill was determined never again to have "DNF" (Did Not Finish) next to his name.

Although he was skeptical, he asked me to work with him as his personal success coach. I assured him it was not too late in life to accomplish this extraordinary undertaking. He put his mind to work by mentally releasing his fear of water, a fear he had learned as a young child, and by editing his past. He then focused on what he wanted to accomplish. I recorded a personal audio program for Bill; for the next three weeks he listened to it daily. He relaxed and used his imagination, mentally preparing for the competition.

What a day it was down in Florida at his next triathlon! The crowd cheered Bill on with a standing ovation as he came up out of the choppy waters of the Gulf of Mexico. He finished the 1.2-mile swim and was ready for the rest of the competition. He had a fantastic experience! He felt strong and exhilarated; he had absolutely no fear of the water. His mind and body worked together perfectly, just as he had imagined. Bill has since participated regularly in triathlons. Now his focus is on swimming faster.

*Overcoming fear is an*
*extraordinary accomplishment!*

## Creating a Memory of Love

Suppose you would like to create a memory that never existed. Why would you want to do this? If you had a childhood lacking in the kind of love and encouragement we all so desperately need, would it help to imagine the ideal situation? Yes! Remember that your analytical, conscious mind knows the facts of reality, but your subconscious mind would feel as though you had the love and support you wanted.

If, for example, as a child you were not hugged or told that you were loved, you could create in your mind the ideal situation. Even though you know that this was not really the way it happened, somehow you begin to notice a change in your feelings. You gain a sense of having been loved and encouraged.

All of these associated thoughts, images, sensations, and feelings are linked together in one of those little packages in the subconscious; it becomes a place where a memory of love is stored. With or without your awareness, this memory may appear just as easily as any memory of a real event; the only difference is you can always count on this one to help you feel better. Feelings are sometimes difficult to explain in words; but nevertheless, feelings are real, even if the source was only imagined. Use your mind to create your own loving memories.

*Changing the way you feel about others,*
*about yourself and your capabilities,*
*is extraordinary!*

## Visualizing Time

I've advised you to leave excess baggage in the past and travel in the direction of your future. Where is the past? Where does the future lie? Let's take a closer look at how our minds store information relating to time.

Most of us have some kind of internal system that allows us to sense time as having a place, or at least a direction, in space. What do I mean by this? You may have a physical sense of how you imagine time that has passed, as well as the time yet to come. You might be able to point to a place in space that describes that sense: up, down, left, right, forward, behind, etc. There is no one correct way to represent time in space. However, assume that the present moment is physically represented where you are in reality (the spot where you are sitting or standing).

Not only can we sense where the past and future are, but some of us also represent other units of time (seconds, minutes, hours, days, weeks, months, and years) in several abstract ways. However, for our purposes here, we will focus only on the past and future in an overall sense.

> EXERCISE: **Locating the Past and Future.** After reading these instructions, stand up and close your eyes. Keep your eyes closed and think about where you sense your past. Does it seem to be behind you, on either side, in front of you, or somewhere else? Just point to where you feel your mind senses the past. Next, point to where you sense the future. Which direction does it seem to be? Go ahead and do this now.

If the directions in which you pointed seem to be okay with you, then remember them as they are. I would suggest that if you pointed to the past as in front of you, or to the ground for the future, you might want to come up with more positive directions for yourself. Once you have done this, you can establish in your mind a physical sense of where you are, in relation to where you have been and the direction in which you are heading.

Why is it important to do this? You can use your mind to symbolically move away from the past and into the future. You can give your inner mind a new set of instructions, in image form, about where you want to go in life. Imagine leaving the negative emotions wherever you sense the past, and moving in the direction of your future, without the excess baggage. See the images, think the thoughts, and feel the feelings of the bad stuff being left behind as you move in a positive direction. Once you do this, from then on, ignore the negative images and focus only on where you want to go.

 *Move away from the past and toward the future.*

# 16

# *Feeling Good about Yourself*

*No one can make you feel inferior without your consent.*

—Eleanor Roosevelt

To find hidden treasures, sometimes all we need to do is look more closely in familiar places and see with new eyes. Try looking at things in different ways than you normally do.

## Finding a Hidden Treasure

Take an ordinary apple. Inside every apple is something besides the sweet fruit, core, and seeds—something that has always been there. Put an apple down on a plate or chopping board; then turn it sideways and cut it in half (through its "equator"). Look inside and find the hidden treasure. (Hint: Notice the design.)

If what you need is to feel good about yourself, then begin to look deeply, through new eyes. See yourself differently and you will find your hidden treasures.

# Are You Your Own Worst Enemy— or Your Best Friend?

Each of us should always be able to count on at least one person to be there for us, no matter what. This person says just what we need to hear, giving the best advice, comforting us, helping us feel better, and accepting and loving us unconditionally. That person can be you! Can you imagine being your own best friend? Most people cannot; they haven't learned yet how valuable and worthwhile they are. Instead they feel undeserving, or that they must be punished; and, who better to do it than themselves? When they look inside, instead of a friend, they find an enemy, a critical, negative sort of person. This inner critic cuts them down every chance he or she gets, calling them names like "Stupid," "Fat Slob," "Ugly," or "Loser." This enemy laughs at them when they try their best and maybe tells them they can't do anything right.

We may get into the habit of hearing negative comments from that inner enemy; and, over time, we can mistakenly accept them as truths. Some of us treat others better than we dare to treat ourselves. Why? Maybe we do this because we learned somewhere along the way that we are not good enough; we feel worthless and undeserving of happiness. If that's what we believe, our subconscious minds will continually remind us of that "truth."

EXERCISE: **Level of Self-Esteem.** Think about the level of your self-esteem. Overall, how good do you feel about yourself? On the following scale (0 = no self-esteem and 10 = very high positive self-esteem), circle the number that represents how you feel about yourself right now. Then ask, "Where do I want to be on the scale?" (Hint: Choose 10. You deserve to feel really good about yourself.)

0   1   2   3   4   5   6   7   8   9   10

EXERCISE: **The Inner Critic.** On a sheet of paper write down five negative statements that you often think or say about yourself. This is the voice of the enemy inside whose sole purpose is to diminish your self-esteem. Keep this; we'll use it again in a moment.

# A Change of Heart

Remember that all of your interpretations and perceptions, including those from your childhood, positive and negative, are stored within your inner mind, and they have created your deep beliefs about yourself and your capabilities. Part of you may *think* one way ("I can do this"), yet you *feel* very differently ("I'm never going to be able to do it"). To feel differently about yourself, to have a change of heart, you need to get rid of the internal critic and rediscover that long-lost best friend. In a way, this process is getting your head and your heart working together in agreement, thinking and feeling the way you want.

> EXERCISE: **Developing a Kind and Loving Voice from Inside.**
> On the same sheet of paper you just used (the list of five negative statements), draw a single line through each negative statement.
>
> One by one, ask yourself "What would my best friend say to me if he or she heard someone tell me this?" Write down the statement that a kind and loving person would say to you to help you feel better. Read each one repeatedly until you commit them to memory and are able say them with your eyes closed.
>
> Close your eyes, take a few belly breaths, and allow yourself to become deeply relaxed. Then repeat these concepts to yourself. Imagine images that go hand in hand with these statements and allow yourself to experience the associated physical and emotional feelings. Let your inner mind absorb these new and better ways of thinking and feeling.

As you create this kind and loving voice from within, whose sole purpose is to help you, you are planting the seeds of self-esteem. With continued reinforcement, these seeds will begin to take root. Soon you will feel a growing sense of acceptance and compassion for yourself.

*What you think about yourself*
*is far more important*
*than what anyone else thinks.*

### "That's Not Like Me!"

We can also take *conscious* control over our critical, negative thoughts about ourselves and replace those damaging messages with words that will eventually change our self-concepts. A very powerful phrase to use is "That's not like me." If at any time you hear that mean inner critic think or say something negative about you, immediately say, silently or aloud, "No! That's not like me to think that way." You may not agree with that positive statement yet, but say it anyway. Then listen to what the caring voice would say to you instead. Each time you do this, you are creating new thought patterns, clearing new pathways in your mental jungle. With repetition, this will become your natural way of thinking. This is a great way to put your conscious mind to work to develop high positive self-esteem.

## Am I Alone?

How we perceive ourselves fitting into our environment is largely determined by how we feel about ourselves deep inside. Many times I have heard individuals say, "I feel separate from everyone else." It seems as if "they" are all in one large group over there, and here I am all alone and different. If only they could understand that most of "them" feel the same way. If all the people who feel separate and different could get together, they would see how many people there are who share similar kinds of feelings.

We all need to feel a connection to something; we need to feel that we are not alone. We must understand that our pain, our struggle to survive, and our hope link us to every other human being. You may have already gained this understanding through your personal religious or spiritual beliefs; however, no matter what those beliefs are, the truth is that you never have to feel alone. Not only is your *best friend* always with you, but so is your *inner child.* Each of them can be a source of total acceptance and unconditional love.

### Someone Is Waiting for You

To feel good about yourself, you need to find and embrace the person you used to be. Each of us starts out in life as lovable and acceptable, but in many cases, the sweet, gentle, loving child within us gets lost, sometimes forever. It's never too late to search for him or her if you know where to look. That precious little one is hiding inside your heart, waiting to be rescued.

Open your heart and get in touch with him or her through your creative imagination. Experience a perfect childhood—laughing, playing, and being happy and carefree. Allow the little girl or boy to feel loved, comforted, and protected by your adult strength. That child deserves to be taken care of and only you can do it! Nurturing your inner child will help give you a sense of purpose and motivate you to take better care of yourself.

## Developing a Sense of Worth

It is possible to connect not only with that inner child, but also with the extraordinary person you were meant to be. You can learn to treat yourself well, the way you deserve to be treated. You can learn to develop a strong sense of self-worth. By now, you know how to put your mind to work to accomplish this task. First, *release the negative patterns* of thinking and behaving. Mentally let go of all of the negative emotions you have carried with you from the past. Secondly, *influence your subconscious*: establish new ways of thinking and feeling by literally bombarding it, while deeply relaxed, with the concepts, images, sensations, and feelings of what you want and need. Create and develop a sense of self-worth, self-respect, unconditional acceptance, and self-love. The idea is not to feel better than others, but at least as good as anyone else.

Last, but not least, begin to *treat yourself well* every day. Be kind and loving to yourself. Think about different things that you would do for a best friend, then do them for yourself. Pretend for a while, if you need to, as you begin to think of yourself as your own best friend. Speak to yourself with words of encouragement and good advice. Never criticize yourself. Always remember that you are doing the best you can; you always have, and you always will. You can only be what you are at certain moments in your life. There is no reason to be mean to yourself. Learn from your mistakes and move on. Ask yourself "Is this the way I would treat someone I cared about?" Start caring about yourself, and you will raise your level of self-esteem. It's not being selfish; it's being sensible! Changing your behavior influences how you think of yourself.

*Treat yourself as though you are*
*AT LEAST as good as anyone else.*

### A Gift For Me?

A long time ago I bought a candle holder for myself. The salesperson asked if this was a gift for someone. I thought, "Well, I guess you could call it a gift, even if it is for me." When I answered, "Yes," she said, "In that case, would you like it gift-wrapped?" I smiled and thought about it for a second, and said, "Absolutely!" It certainly would be something I would do for a person I cared about. I was excited about my gift. When I returned home, I put it on the table and looked at it for a few hours, enjoying the thoughtfulness of my best friend. I finally opened the pretty package; it was exactly what I had wanted! I've come a long way to be with my best friend again; I'm never going to let her go! With her around, I never feel alone.

Treat yourself well; and, over time you will begin to feel that you are a valuable and worthwhile human being. You will believe that you deserve to have a special friend in your heart, one who is always there for you.

Let's do a few more exercises that will help you not only understand more about yourself, but also how to develop a sense of self-respect and appreciation.

EXERCISE: **Your Hands.** Put this book down and hold up both hands in front of you. Turn them over so you get a good look at both sides. What is the first thought that comes to your mind about them? What is the next thing you think about?

If you are like most people, you probably made at least one negative remark about your hands: ugly fingernails, wrinkled skin, brown spots, etc. Notice whether your first thought was a negative or positive one.

Each of us has a tendency to lean one way or the other. We automatically look for and focus on either positive or negative aspects, no matter what the subject is. Become aware of which one you tend to do most often. If your thoughts centered on what was wrong with your hands, consider taking another look. This time focus on finding something good to say.

> ### *Remember to focus like a laser on the good things!*

Did you think about how your hands helped you accomplish something extraordinary, such as comforting someone and wiping away their tears? Did you think about how your hands held the hand of a loved one, or how hard they worked to make something special? The next time you look at your hands, think, "How wonderful these hands are! How useful they have been!" Begin to focus more on the "good stuff." Over time you can form new habits. Look for the good in something and you will find it; do that often enough and you will change your thought patterns. After a while, you will naturally look for something positive first, not only in yourself, but also in everything around you, and in all your situations.

EXERCISE: **Things I Like About Myself.** Write down at least three things that you like about yourself. As you reflect on these, begin to appreciate your good qualities. Use these statements while you are relaxed to reinforce your sense of value.

EXERCISE: **Things I Have Done Successfully.** Write down at least three things that you have successfully completed. (Realize that each one is extraordinary; *all* accomplishments are.) Reflect on these. Allow yourself to feel a sense of accomplishment no matter how much may still lie ahead.

EXERCISE: **Searching Your Heart.** Search your heart for your deepest feelings in completing the following statements. (Writing them down is a good idea.)

My greatest fear is _____.

My greatest need is _____.

My greatest desire is _____.

As you reflect on your deepest fear, need, and desire, you are bringing into focus what is important to you. It may be interesting to compare these responses to the values you marked in Chapter 3. Do they seem to match? If not, you may want to consider changing your priorities. Use what you know about yourself now to become more of who you want to be. Solidify in your mind and heart who you are and what is important to you. Take that knowledge and create your ideal future.

Remember to focus on those things that are in your control. Decide to spend your time and energy on extraordinary accomplishments: overcoming obstacles, and bringing into your life all that you need and want. Decide to make your life better, then do it!

## How to Be Happy

When I ask people, "What do you want?" the response I get most often is ". . . just to be happy." Essential to being happy is having a strong sense of who you are and feeling good about yourself. When you have that, all that's left for you to do is to *be yourself* (and let others be themselves).

The wisdom of the Chinese philosopher Lao-tzu reminds us that, in order for us to be happy, we should be more like nature and do everything for nothing. The rose blooms of its own free will and asks no reward. Go out into the world and bloom like the rose. (And aren't roses extraordinary?)

*Be all that you are and expect nothing from anyone but yourself.*

# 17

# *Putting Your Mind to Work*

*It is not enough to be busy. The question is:
What are we busy about?*

—HENRY DAVID THOREAU

I t's not what you know that's important, it's what you do with what you know. Realizing what must be done to move ahead, and actually doing those things are two separate entities.

Self-improvement is a lifelong process. By following the steps outlined in this chapter, you can take more control over your life, and make improvements in specific areas, one at a time. At this point, you know a great deal about the mind and what it takes to create positive changes. Ideally, you know more about yourself and are open to possibilities. You may have the desire to change at least one thing in your life, to accomplish something extraordinary. Hopefully, you have been inspired and are motivated enough to travel forward, to put some of what you know into practice. You are ready to gain more of *The Inside Advantage*.

# Steps to Follow for
# Maximum Results

When you have a specific area to work on, use these steps:

1. **Find a peaceful environment and set aside time.** Choose a place where you can be free of distractions and a time when it is unlikely that you will be interrupted. Allow approximately 20–30 minutes. You may find that soothing music or certain sounds such as wind chimes, ocean waves, or rainfall help to block out distracting noises.

2. **Relax and make yourself as comfortable as you can.** You may find it helpful to sit back in a comfortable chair or recliner, and separate your feet about ten or twelve inches, with your arms on the armrests.

3. **Close your eyes.** Remove visual distractions by gently lowering your eyelids; you will want to keep your eyes closed throughout the process. Consider using a mask for your eyes to block out any light. This may also help to reduce the muscle tension in and around your eyes.

4. **Begin by breathing deeply.** You can breathe either through your nose or mouth, whatever is comfortable for you. I start off inhaling through my nose and exhaling through my mouth. After a few deep breaths, just breathe naturally. Every now and then you can take a full breath to deepen your relaxation.

5. **Become very still, except for your breathing.** Without movement, there is less information for your brain to process. You may find that, after several minutes of relaxing this way, your head and body almost feel disconnected; it's an interesting sensation. If you experience this, there is no need to be concerned; it's useful feedback. It simply means that you are becoming less aware of your body and more deeply relaxed.

6. **Begin to focus on one thing at a time.** Clear your mind of distracting thoughts, pushing them away gently. You could imagine putting your thoughts in bubbles and letting them float away.

(See Chapter 7 for ideas.) Be patient with yourself as you narrow your focus of awareness.

7. **Relax your muscles and let your mind become carefree.** The technique involving sending messages from your mind to your muscles will work best here; it requires no movement. Imagine your muscles becoming warm, loose, and relaxed. You can focus on different parts of the body as you completely let go of muscle tension, a little at a time. Sense a feeling of heaviness as you imagine sinking down into a very deep state of relaxation.

Spend a few minutes imagining or recalling a peaceful place where you can leave your cares and concerns behind. At this point your mind is much more open and receptive. The conscious "guard" at the filtering gate of the subconscious is very likely looking the other way or has gone on break, allowing new concepts and images to slip right in without being analyzed or judged.

8. **Create specific thoughts, images, sensations, and feelings.** Focus on and visualize what you want to accomplish by using your extraordinary imagination. This could include: (a) positive statements and concepts affirming the beliefs you want to establish, (b) ideal mental images for your specific needs (perhaps switching perspectives), (c) natural, healthy physical sensations in your body, and (d) desirable emotional feelings, such as strength, confidence, power, freedom, etc. Other than for immediate needs, when you finish reading this book, you may want to use the "Extraordinary Changes Questionnaire" (in the Appendix) for ideas.

Think the thoughts, mentally see or sense the images, feel the physical sensations, and experience the emotions that you need and want. Remember to focus on what you want as opposed to what you don't want. (Notice that I said, "remember" rather than "Don't forget!") After approximately 20–30 minutes, slowly return to the beta state (broad awareness), and open your eyes. If you are visualizing to help with a situation occurring in the present moment, continue for as long as you need.

9. **Expect the outcome to occur as you envision it.** Be open to the possibilities of what your mind can achieve. Almost anything is possible!

10. **Use repetition.** The more you are exposed to something, the more you are influenced by it; it's a natural process. By repeating concepts, continuing to hold specific images in your mind, and experiencing certain sensations and feelings over and over again, you begin to develop new ways of thinking, feeling, and behaving. Literally bombard your subconscious mind with what you want to experience. Listening to audio tapes can make this process much easier. You can create your own or use programs designed to meet specific needs.

Research tells us that it takes approximately 21–30 days to establish a new habit. What is a habit? It's simply something we do on a regular basis. Remember that it is the function of the subconscious mind to create habits for us. We can retrain our minds through repetition. It is essential that reinforcement continue for 21–30 consecutive days. After that initial period, occasional reinforcement may still be needed.

For changes such as learning to treat yourself as your own best friend, gaining confidence, or enhancing wellness, it makes sense to follow Steps 1–10. When all you need is to put your mind to work in the present moment to temporarily change the current situation (such as escaping from pain at the dentist's office), simply go through Steps 2–8. Use common sense to determine which steps seem appropriate for your needs. The more you practice deep relaxation and creative visualization, the easier it becomes. Not only can you create long-lasting positive changes, but you can also learn to take control more quickly and easily whenever you need to.

*Practice, Practice, Practice!!!*
*Train your mind*
*to work for you automatically.*

Remember that to go from ordinary to extraordinary, a transformation must occur in your thoughts (how you think), in your beliefs (what you feel in your heart), and in your actions (what you do). When you put your mind to work, you not only alter the way you think, but you also change your feelings and behaviors. In this process you are taking more control over your life. You will discover that you can do anything you put your mind to, if it's in your control, and you want it badly enough. René Descartes, a 17th century French philosopher said, "It is not enough to have a good mind. The main thing is to use it well."

# 18

# *What Else?*

*The greatest discovery of my generation is that human beings, by changing the inner attitudes of their minds, can change the outer aspects of their lives.*

—William James

We have covered quite a bit of ground, delving into how you can gain *The Inside Advantage.* You can jump-start your life, personally and professionally, and become the person you have always wanted to be. You know how to be healthier, happier, and more successful. You may already be developing an "Oh, wow!" attitude. Remember that it's never too early, or too late, to travel on a different road, and, if you have a map, the journey is easy. Going where you have never been before can be very exciting!

Think about the areas in your life in which you would like to do things differently. This chapter will provide you with more ideas as to where you can put your mind to work for your benefit.

*It's never too early or
too late to get started.*

## Peak Job Performance

If you tap into your inner resources for help with memory, concentration, and testing, you can reach higher levels in your career. You can also be more productive in your work if you train yourself to sleep well and to successfully cope with stress. You can also use your inner mind to enhance creativity, and improve your problem-solving and decision-making abilities.

Achieving peak job performance is much easier and more natural when there is no distinction between the work you do and who you are. Your head and heart are working together in agreement: what you think you should be doing and what you feel that you want to do are the same. If this is not the case, try using receptive visualizations to discover how you can best serve your purpose, with talents that are uniquely yours.

## Memory, Concentration, and Test Taking

Areas where it seems natural to apply *The Inside Advantage* are memory, concentration, and test taking. I used these techniques and earned a 4.0 grade point average in graduate school. I now work with many students and professionals to help them put their minds to work to reach their highest potentials.

A promotion in the United States Air Force to Master Sergeant would mean total accomplishment to Pat, who was a Technical Sergeant when he asked for my help with mental training. He had taken the promotional tests three times before and was unable to reach the cutoff point. Determined to pass on his fourth attempt, he put his mind to work like never before. I created and recorded a personal audio program for him, which he used for several weeks to prepare mentally. Finally, it was time to prove that he could do it. During the testing, he felt relaxed, confident, and in control. His concentration was focused, and he easily recalled the information he had studied. He felt good about his performance and anxiously awaited word from his commander about his results. Two months later, during morning roll call, there was a surprise announcement; Pat was singled out as "... a shining example, an exceptional performer." He not only passed, he scored forty points higher than the last time! How proud he and his family were when the commander pinned his stripes on his sleeves.

## Increasing Sales

Fear of rejection and failure, and even fear of success, hold us back from accomplishing extraordinary things in our careers. If you are in the business of selling a product or service, do you feel totally confident? Do you procrastinate when it comes to making the contacts you need to generate business? You know too well how annoying it can be when the phone rings repeatedly as others are trying to market their businesses to you. You don't want to be bothered and, in turn, you may feel that your calls are bothering others. You almost expect them to say, "No" and hang up. Of course, no one likes to be rejected in any situation. It touches a chord deep inside us, and we begin to doubt ourselves and our capabilities. When this happens, we find it difficult to be productive and to feel successful.

It may seem odd to talk about having a fear of success, but for many people this is exactly the case. Part of us may think that we want to be successful, but another part may feel threatened by the possibility. If we have a deep belief that we cannot be successful, or that we don't deserve success, our subconscious minds will manifest those beliefs in our behaviors. We will find ways to sabotage ourselves, either keeping success at bay or destroying what we have already accomplished. This is much more common than most people realize.

If you have a fear of success, perhaps as a child or young person, one of the comments you often heard was "You'll never amount to anything." At the time, you didn't know any better, so that information was accepted and stored in your subconscious mind as a truth, a belief about your capabilities. When you think you might be able to accomplish something, your inner mind reminds you that you cannot. You think one way, yet feel another. You learn to doubt yourself and are unable to move forward.

Even though you may not consciously understand the motivating reasons behind your actions, you can still make changes within yourself. You can learn that you have what it takes and that you deserve to be successful. You can feel confident and motivated to do what's needed to get ahead. By now you know how to use your mind to do these things—get rid of the excess baggage, replace fear with confidence, and plant the seeds of success. Repetition of the concepts, images, and feelings of what you want to accomplish will help you believe in yourself and commit to excellence.

## Public Speaking

If speaking in front of others is difficult for you (the mere thought of it makes you feel queasy), then you are like most people. Have you ever waited your turn as introductions were being made around the room? You knew soon you were going to have to stand and say your name, where you work, what you do, and so forth. Did your heart beat faster? Did you begin to breathe quickly? Were your palms perspiring? Did you experience butterflies fluttering around in your stomach? Your body was preparing to deal with a situation you perceived as stressful. Your body was following your thoughts and the associated images. You may have thought to yourself, "What if I turn red? I don't want to look foolish? What will they think if my mind goes blank? What if they don't like me?" Does this sound familiar? If it does, know that you are not alone.

What's important for you to know is that regardless of how nervous you may feel in that type of situation, or for that matter, whenever you have to give a presentation, you can gain a higher level of self-confidence. Don't let fear stop you! You must, first of all, believe that you have something of value to say. (Everyone does!) When your passion to share who you are and what's in your heart with others becomes stronger than your fear of public speaking, you will be able to find the courage to do it. You can make it easier on yourself by practicing deep relaxation and mentally rehearsing your performance. This will reinforce the appropriate thoughts, images, sensations, and feelings. You will begin to hear a supportive and encouraging voice from within. By creating the ideal reality in your mind repeatedly, when you get up to speak, you will feel as if you have already done it successfully many times.

## Enhancing Sports Performance

The mind plays a major role in any sport. In order to perform well we must be prepared not only physically, but also mentally. Sports performance of all kinds can be enhanced through the practice of relaxation and visualization. Imagine peak performance as you play your favorite sport in your mind, whether your game is golf, tennis, swimming, bowling, gymnastics, or running. Do you remember Bill, the triathlete? He trained his mind and body to work together.

It's been said that golf, as well as many other sports, is about 20 percent physical and 80 percent mental self-programming. A seminar that I conduct for golfers (professionals and amateurs) is called "Mastering Golf Skills;" it has been approved by the national Professional Golf Association (PGA) for education credits for members. There is also an audio program of the same name designed for visualizing all aspects of golf: the fundamental skills, as well as relaxation, enjoyment, confidence, and concentration. One of my clients who had mentally practiced for about thirty days hit his first hole-in-one. He was so excited! His name appeared in the sports section of the newspaper; his friends were congratulating him. When I spoke to him, he whispered to me that he was not about to admit to anyone that his success had anything to do with the recorded program. We both knew better! That's why in our advertising we say, "Who in your foursome has 'The Inside Advantage®' and isn't telling?" Recently my husband also hit his first hole-in-one on a championship course. His comment was "This really works!"

## Limitless Possibilities

Know that the possibilities are limitless as to how you can apply this information and these techniques. When you take control over one thing in your life, and make changes in the way you think, how you feel, and what you do, that helps to build a new belief system. It says that you can do just about anything you put your mind and heart into.

 *By believing in yourself and putting your mind to work like never before, you can accomplish extraordinary things.*

# 19

# *Lagniappe— Something Extra*

Growing up in New Orleans, a word I heard often was *lagniappe* (pronounced "lan yap"); it is American-French and means "something extra and unexpected." So consider this chapter something extra, a bonus: a few last thoughts that you might be able to use on your extraordinary journey.

## If You Love Someone, Tell Them

I remember the last time I saw my grandmother alive; she was in the hospital and very sick. She was a special person in my life. I think she must have known that this would be our last visit; she held my hand and told me she loved me. It was the first time I heard her say that. I had known it, but it was so wonderful hearing those special words. The next time I held her hand, she had already passed away; but I could still hear her sweet words echoing in my heart.

A few years later, when I was 27 years old, I returned home from class at the university. The professor had discussed sharing feelings and communicating with those who are close to us. He suggested that we go home and tell the people we love, simply "I love you." I was already in the habit of saying that to my husband and son. Then I thought about my parents, my sister, and brother. I had never told them that, nor do I remember ever hearing it from them. Could I do it? I was strangely uncomfortable with the idea. I knew in my heart I loved them, but saying it aloud was quite different.

My body trembled as I dialed the phone to reach my parents in New Orleans. Why was it so hard? My heart pounded as my mother answered. My dad picked up the other phone at the same time. "Hi! It's me. I called to tell both of you . . . (pause) I love you." There! I had said it! I wondered how they would respond. There was a long silence. My dad told me he would get off the phone now so I could talk to Mom, and Mom said that she was glad I called and would talk to me later. Then she hung up.

I stood there holding the phone and crying. "At least I've said it," I thought to myself. A few minutes later they called back. They were both on the phone again. I heard them say, "We love you, too." The three of us cried together; we talked about how we wanted to start saying that from then on. Don't let a day go by without saying those three words to the special people in your life.

*Say what you mean and*
*mean what you say.*

## If You Love Someone, Show Affection

While my mom, dad, and I were on the phone, I also mentioned that I wanted to start hugging and holding hands when we were together. I don't recall doing any of that growing up. It didn't matter why that was not part of our family traditions; that was just the way it was. The next time I visited them was one of the best visits of all. We hugged, kissed, held hands, and said, "I love you." It was what my heart had longed for. Since then, we never miss a chance to let each other know how much we care.

*It's never too late to touch
someone's heart.*

# Help Yourself by Helping Others

### Volunteer

When you are in need of compassion, understanding, and a sense of purpose, one of the best things you can do for yourself is to do something for someone else. No matter what your situation, helping others is a great source of joy. What you gain from volunteering your time and energy far exceeds what you give. Many organizations exist for the sole purpose of helping others. Look and you will find them. Contact hospitals, nursing homes, local nonprofit organizations; they are all in need of people wanting to help. Especially during holidays, if you are feeling sad, turn your focus toward others and their needs for a while. You will find that your spirits will be uplifted, too.

I began volunteering for the first time as an adult, teaching people with illnesses about relaxation and visualization. I remember experiencing one of the happiest moments of my life when I volunteered at a wellness workshop for people who were seriously ill.

One of the activities was called an "Angel Walk" (some called it "Angel Wash"). This involved all participants and volunteers (about fifty people). Each of us had an opportunity to walk, one at a time, down a path flanked on both sides by everyone else. As each person walked slowly with their eyes closed, everyone in the two lines offered some act of kindness—a touch on the shoulder, a hug, a squeeze of the hand, and usually words from the heart. It was not important to see what was going on as you walked along, only to feel it. There was a shower of positive energy and love for everyone involved. This was one of the most memorable experiences I have ever had. Not only was I able to give something from my heart to others, but I also received an enormous outpouring of love from everyone there. We know that love helps to heal lives. Volunteer when you can. Create extraordinary experiences for yourself and others.

**Commit Random Acts of Kindness**

Do something nice for someone without expecting anything in return. Jennings Osborne is a philanthropist who spreads cheer in many ways, one of which is providing light displays at Walt Disney World during the Christmas holidays. He and his family put a billboard up in his hometown, challenging everyone to commit random acts of kindness. Look for ways to brighten someone's day and you will experience more joy, too.

While attending a National Speakers Association convention in Philadelphia, I bought a dozen roses. When the florist asked me who they were for, I smiled and said, "I don't know yet." When I returned to the hotel, I began handing them out to individuals, some of whom I didn't even know. This was a way for me to share with others the joy I was experiencing. I felt a sensation of spiraling upward; the more I gave, the more I received. I invite you to commit random acts of kindness as often as you can.

 *Once you start giving to others,*
*you won't want to stop.*

## We Are Never Promised Our Next Breath, So Make the Most of Every Day

Mahatma Gandhi said, "Live each day as if you would die tomorrow. Learn each day as if you would live forever."

We can learn the same lesson from nature about life's brevity. Consider two of Mother Nature's treasures: the morning glory and the moon flower. Both from the same family, they bloom only for a few hours, yet their delicate beauty is extraordinary. The sweet fragrance of the moon flower will not soon be forgotten. Unless we stop to notice them, they're gone before we realize that we missed them.

We tend to take our futures for granted; all the time we need or want seems to be out there ahead of us. We put things off; we'll do it tomorrow. Sometimes tomorrow never comes. My niece, Tina, a 26-year-old mother of two young children, recently passed away. Three weeks earlier she was thrown from her car as it went off the road and rolled over. (Please wear your seat belts!) Jay, an 18-year-old, and one of my son's best friends, drove into the path of an oncoming car and died shortly thereafter. At a family reunion we watched in horror as a two-year-old relative fell down the stairwell to his death. Certainly you have your share of sorrowful stories and lost loved ones. I mention these not to sadden you, but to inspire you to live as if each day were your last. Know, however, that sadness stretches your capacity to feel deeply, not only the depths of despair, but also heightened moments of profound joy. Death can be a great teacher of appreciation and compassion for all that is alive, including ourselves. It reminds us what is truly important.

When I was reading the book *On Death and Dying* by Elisabeth Kübler-Ross, M.D., my husband walked into the room and saw tears streaming down my cheeks. He asked, "Why do you read books that make you sad?" I quickly responded, "You don't understand. It's not about dying; it's about living." My tears were not of sorrow and pain, but were tears of joy.

Every chance I have, I wave "good-bye" and throw a kiss to my loved ones as they drive away. I think, "If this is the last time I see you, here's one more reminder of how much you mean to me." I urge you to grow your relationships with the people who are special to you. Make each day count. Be aware of the treasure that today is. Learn from it and savor the special moments.

 *Love and live deeply.*

I wrote a poem for my son just after he left for college; it was difficult letting go. Not only do the following words speak of seizing the moment, but also of love, appreciation, and using your imagination.

Now and Then

The cool breeze blows gently across my face;
I close my eyes and instantly
I'm back in time, another place.

I see a little boy smiling, full of energy,
quietly on his way to becoming a man,
only it seems so far away.

Then, but not now. Today he's grown,
and my heart is filled with memories of
that boy and happy times together.

The sun comes in the window
as afternoon makes its way to evening.
No one sits at the table today to play games,
but I remember.

I pass by the old house, lake, and school;
scenes come rushing back to fill my mind
and heart all at once.
I smile and cry at the same time:
Such joy for all that's been!
Such sweet sorrow
because I can't hold that little hand
and look down into his dark eyes,
and be "Mom" again in the same way.

To be needed and loved by a child
growing in wonder at life's gifts is a gift itself.
And I'm thankful, not just for then,
but as always, for now.

## Listen to Your Heart

I have learned that when I hear what seems to be a clear voice from deep within, I should listen. For you, it may be a gut feeling, intuition, or some kind of signal urging you to do something, or perhaps, not to do something. It's the voice that you know to be true, right, and good. Trust its authenticity; you don't need to understand how or why it speaks to you, or even its source. The important thing is to pay attention to it, accept it, and heed its advice. Listen and learn; have faith that its purpose is to guide you on your journey.

## Last, But Not Least— Dare to Live Successfully!

People may appear successful if you look at their jobs, the amount of money they make, and their material possessions. However, many of these people haven't a clue about the meaning of success; they don't understand that success without significance is not success. Deepak Chopra, M.D., author of several books including *The Seven Spiritual Laws of Success*, eloquently defines true success as ". . . the ability to love and have compassion, the capacity to experience joy and spread it to others, the security of knowing your life has meaning and purpose, and a sense of connection to the creative power of the universe—whatever you want to call it."

Congratulations! By now, you know that you have read this book for a reason, or perhaps for several reasons. Many seeds have been planted in your mind, and like wildflower seeds, which can lie dormant for years, they will grow when the time is right. A Chinese proverb says, "The flowers of all of our tomorrows are in the seeds of today." When you are ready, you will take action to change the way you think and feel, and ultimately what you do (one project at a time). The knowledge, insight, and understanding you have gained can have an enormous influence over how you experience your future. You have the map you need to take this journey. On the way, you will accomplish extraordinary things. Eventually, if not already, you will understand that everything you have ever needed is already within you.

Accept and love yourself for all that you are, in spite of your flaws. Become your own best friend and treat yourself well.

Discover your hidden treasures. Believe in yourself and commit to excellence. Celebrate life's journey, step by step, each precious moment. Live joyfully and successfully! Dare mighty things!

## *YOU are extraordinary!*

# APPENDIX

# About the Author

## Cathy Wenzel Lauro

I was born at a very young age in New Orleans . . . no, wait, that's going back too far. How's this? I'm just an ordinary person who has learned how to accomplish some extraordinary things. One of the lessons I needed desperately to learn in life was that I was a valuable and worthwhile human being, that I was at least as good as other people. Growing up I felt inferior to everyone else. It seemed that nothing I ever did was good enough. I couldn't be perfect, no matter how hard I tried. I remember saying to myself, "You are nothing." I thought I was nothing, I believed I was nothing, and I acted like I was nothing. Certainly I didn't deserve to be happy. Talk about faulty thinking!

When I realized that it was my responsibility to take control of my life, things began to change. When I was 20 years old, my dad started buying me self-improvement books; he knew how unhappy I was. Not long after that, I attended a workshop on the power of the mind. I was hooked! All I wanted to study was how our minds work. I wanted to know what made me the way I was and what makes other people act the way they do. I began a lifelong journey, a quest, seeking more answers, not only to know "why," but "how." How could I make changes for the better? Along the way it became clear to me that I had to focus only on those things that were in my control. I wanted and needed to focus on changing myself—my thoughts, feelings, and behaviors. Self-improvement is a never-ending journey.

Of course, I majored in psychology in college. After nine years, mostly as a part-time student, I earned a Bachelor's degree and a Master's in Applied Psychology. For ten years I worked in corporate management in training and human resources. After a life-changing event, a very personal and emotional experience that I often share with audiences, I reevaluated my life and my priorities. I made major changes that affected everything. My life has been spiraling upward ever since!

I take pride in my affiliation with the National Speakers Association. I give presentations, conduct seminars and workshops, and for several years have taught university-sponsored classes. As an author, professional speaker, trainer, and consultant, I am dedicated to teaching others not only how to use their minds more effectively, but also how to live more joyfully and successfully. I hope to inspire others to make a difference in their own lives. As a personal success coach I enjoy helping individuals achieve their goals, whatever those might be. I help them change the way they think, feel, and ultimately what they do. My aim is to help you believe, deep in your heart, that you can accomplish anything you set out to do, if it's in your control.

I am thrilled to be involved in work that I truly love; in fact, I can honestly say that I would do it even if I didn't get paid for it. When you have a passion for your work, there is no distinction between what you do for a living and who you are. The great stage actress Caitlin Hart pointed out to me that whenever I am speaking, and now writing, someone's soul is listening; and, for that privilege, I will always be truly grateful.

Throughout this book I have shared with you insights from my own personal journey. I hope that I have not only exposed you to different ways of thinking, but that I have also touched your heart and inspired you to make a difference for yourself. Now, I'll let you in on a little secret: you were never ordinary to begin with!

I wish for you inner strength, peace of mind,
moments of joy, and love.

*Cathy*

**As a Professional Speaker:**

Cathy is dedicated to helping others not only learn how to use their minds more effectively for personal and professional development, but also to live more joyfully and successfully. Cathy provides you with the tools you need to change the way you think, how you feel, and what you do. Her audiences are enlightened, entertained, and inspired! Cathy is a warm, charismatic, motivational speaker and educator, whose interactive presentations deliver positive strategies for success. With her enthusiasm and thought-provoking concepts . . .

**Cathy will not only make you think,
she will touch your heart in a special way!**

> *"Your warmth and sincerity, as well as your enthusiasm and professionalism, make it easy to see that you have a passion for what you do. You gave us many practical techniques that can be put to use immediately. We were very satisfied with your presentation. Our telecast was a success!"*
>
> Dillard's, Inc., Stress Management Program, nationwide satellite telecast for sales managers

# Popular Keynotes, Seminars, and Workshops

Gain *The Inside Advantage*

Learn How You Can
Accomplish Extraordinary Things

- *Let Go, Lighten Up, and Get On With It* ™
  Stress Relief and More

- *Creating Success from the Inside Out* ™
  Strategies for Personal and Professional Success

- *Mind-Body Wellness* ™
  Promote Optimal Health and Well-Being

- *Mastering Golf Skills* ™
  Improve Your Game (PGA approved)

These programs can be customized to fit your
organization's needs and interests.

A Self-Empowerment Workshop

## "The Inside Advantage" Weekend Experience

Step Back and Take a Closer Look

*Learn How You Can Accomplish Extraordinary Things*

On-Going
Personal Development Programs
(Small Group Interaction)

Spring and Fall
Friday evening through Sunday noon

**Extraordinary Things Are
Within Your Reach!**

Come alone or bring a friend!

Call for dates, location, and prices
(501) 224-0040

# The Inside Advantage®
## Audio Programs

The Inside Advantage® audio programs cover a variety of topics to help individuals achieve specific goals. They are absolutely unique! The exceptional quality of these programs comes from paying close attention to detail. Much time is spent carefully choosing just the right words, concepts, and imagery for their special meanings.

The original, rhythmic music was created by my sister, Dezlie Wenzel Fried (pronounced Freed), a talented musician from New Orleans. Listeners say they absolutely love the music; it's mesmerizing! Also, captivating and gently pulsating tones can be heard in the background. (Nothing is subliminal; you hear everything.) These are synchronized to the brain wave patterns we naturally experience when we are deeply relaxed. The beat of the music and the tones work automatically to help you feel calm, comfortable, and carefree.

As you listen, you are invited to let go of your stress, your cares and concerns, as my voice gently soothes and lulls you into a wonderfully peaceful state of serenity, in both your mind and body. After a short while, your awareness will become much more focused (in the alpha-theta range, somewhere between waking and sleeping), where your mind is at peak receptivity for creating positive changes. *Sleep Well* is designed to help you reach deep sleep more easily, therefore the tones are slower and are synchronized to the brain wave patterns you normally experience when you are in deep sleep.

The programs are professionally produced in digital stereo (with the exception of personalized programs). On some tapes you will find an informative "Introduction" on one side. This may be listened to at any time, with your eyes open. Programs range in length from approximately 20–40 minutes. Some of the taped programs are identical on both sides for continuous play.

When listening to each program, you'll want to make yourself comfortable, sitting or reclining, in a quiet environment. You will hear my voice, background music, the tones, and special sound effects, all of which enhance relaxation and listening pleasure. Programs are intended for listening through *headphones,* with your *eyes closed.* WARNING: **DO NOT** listen to the Program Side(s) while driving a vehicle, operating machinery, or while involved in an activity that requires you to be fully alert. To obtain the maximum benefit, plan to reinforce the relaxation, concepts, images, physical sensations, and emotional feelings by listening initially for 21–30 consecutive days. After that, you can listen as often as you like. Take advantage of your own inner human resources. Train your mind to work for you for a change.

### RELAXATION AND PERSONAL GOALS
The idea for this program came from my students in a course on creative visualization. They said that it was easy to do the exercises in class, but they needed something to help them relax and focus on their own at home. They also wanted to hear the music I used in the classroom. Thus, the audio program *Escape to Serenity* was born. With this program, you will be able to easily practice focusing and relaxing. The guided imagery will help you escape in your mind (and body), and to feel carefree. While you are deeply relaxed (at alpha-theta) you will be given an opportunity to insert your own personal imagery for your specific needs.

### WELLNESS
*Visualizing Radiant Health* is the audio program specifically designed to help you focus your energy on sensing wellness within your body. You may only have a minor problem, such as a cold or a tight muscle. Perhaps you are recovering from an illness or surgery; you can work to hasten the healing process. This program can be used by those who are seriously ill and want to feel better. It is also for people who are well and want to focus on staying that way. Let the soothing imagery guide your mind, as your body follows your thoughts.

### CHEMOTHERAPY AND RADIATION THERAPY
*(two separate programs)*
For individuals undergoing chemotherapy, the soothing audio program *River of Sunlight* is for use especially during treatment. *Rays of Sunlight* is a separate program for those needing radiation therapy. Both of these can be used throughout the course of treatment. Specific guided imagery helps you not only relax, but is

also designed to get your mind and body working together to enhance treatment efficiency, wellness, comfort, and peace of mind. The same program is recorded on both sides for your convenience; let it play continuously for as long as you need it.

## HIV AND AIDS

As a member of the Board of Directors for the Ryan White Center, I conduct workshops for those living with HIV and AIDS. My aim is to help individuals understand how they can use their minds to enhance the quality of their lives. From this work came the audio program *Relaxation, Imagery, and Positive Concepts for HIV/ AIDS.* It is designed to help listeners cope with stress, gain peace of mind, and raise their levels of self-esteem. Also included is imagery specifically related to the virus and for strengthening the immune system.

## SLEEP

*Sleep Well* was created through my work with individuals who had insomnia—problems falling asleep, staying asleep, and sleeping deeply. The audible tones in this particular program are noticeably different from those in the alpha-theta range. They are synchronized to delta brain wave patterns (those experienced in deep sleep). They invite your brain to get in step with delta waves. Guided imagery, as well as the beat of the music, tones, and special sound effects help to lull listeners into a natural deeply relaxed state of mind and body. With practice, you are training your mind and body to establish a new and beneficial pattern of sleeping.

Also related to sleep is Fibromyalgia Syndrome (pronounced "fie-bro-my-al'-jia"). The book *Fibromyalgia & Chronic Myofacial Pain Syndrome* by Devin Starlanyl, M.D. and Mary Ellen Copeland, M.S., M.A., helps us understand more about this condition. It is a common form of generalized muscular pain and fatigue; approximately five million people in the United States are affected.

Normally, our deepest sleep is basically uninterrupted delta waves, unless, according to research, the individual has fibromyalgia. In this case, alpha brain waves intrude during delta sleep and can cause chronic sleep deprivation, which in turn worsens chronic pain. The individuals suffering with fibromyalgia with whom I have worked have found some relief listening to *Escape to Serenity* or *Visualizing Radiant Health* during the day, and *Sleep Well* at night. Deep sleep is exactly what is needed by those with fibromyalgia.

INCREASING SALES

People who are in the business of selling products or services need to feel that nothing stands in their way of phenomenal success. However, their beliefs about themselves and their capabilities may hold them back from making quantum leaps in their careers. The fear of rejection by prospects or clients may keep them from making as many contacts as possible. Procrastination becomes a routine part of their day. Perhaps they fear a certain level of success. In this case they will somehow unintentionally cause themselves to fail. The audio program *Breaking Sales Barriers* is designed to help individuals in sales not only overcome the fear of success and rejection, but also to believe in themselves and commit to excellence.

ENHANCING GOLF PERFORMANCE

To perform well in any sport we must be prepared not only physically, but also mentally. Studies show that performance can be enhanced through the practice of relaxation and visualization. Imagine playing golf in your mind, where every shot is perfect. The audio program, *Mastering Golf Skills* was designed for visualizing all aspects of golf: fundamental skills (alignment, swing, pitching, chipping, sand shots, and putting), as well as relaxation, enjoyment, confidence, and concentration. This program is based on extensive research and was created for both beginners and experienced golfers. It goes hand-in-hand with the course of the same name, which has been approved by the national Professional Golf Association (PGA) for education credits for members. Please specify either the left- or right-handed version when ordering.

PERSONALIZED VISUALIZATION PROGRAMS

For years I have created personalized imagery programs for individuals to help them accomplish extraordinary things. Each program is designed to meet your specific needs. During the process, relevant data is gathered through a variety of ways. This information is used to develop the concepts and images that you want and need to hear. An audio program is then recorded. It is designed for listening through headphones, as you relax with your eyes closed.

You know that the more often you are exposed to something, the more you are influenced by it. Remember that you move in the direction of your dominant thoughts. In this way, you are literally bombarding your subconscious mind with the thoughts, images, sensations, and feelings that you need in order to accomplish exactly what you want. It's like rewriting the script of the inner dialog that goes on inside your head. Over time, you begin to naturally change the way you think and feel, and ultimately what you do. Having your program personalized makes it very easy for you; your only job is to put headphones on, relax, and allow your mind to absorb the information. In this way, you effortlessly gain *The Inside Advantage*®.

Audio programs can be customized and personalized to meet your, or your organization's, specific needs. Let me know how I can help you.

To Order
The Inside Advantage® Audio Programs
or for information on other available
Learning Resources
Call  (501) 224-0040

# Personal Success Coaching

Helping You Change the Way You Think,
How You Feel, and What You Do

Meeting Your Specific Needs

## Telephone Consultations

Personal Coaching for 3 months (once a week)

## Private Consultation and
## Personalized Recorded Program

Evaluation Questionnaire
Private Consultation
Personalized Recorded Audio Program

\* \* \* \* \* \* \*

Call (501) 224-0040 for:

Speaking Engagements / Keynotes
Seminars and Workshops
Corporate Training
Consulting
Personal Success Coaching
Learning Resources

# About the Extraordinary Changes Questionnaire™

This questionnaire is designed to help you in the process of charting your course for change, one step at a time. It will allow you to reflect not only on your desires and motivations, but also on your past and present situations. You will also have an opportunity to consider how you envision your future. Your responses can be a source of valuable information and insight that will help you accomplish extraordinary things. Also, they may provide you with ideas that you can use in visualizing.

You'll probably want to use a few sheets of paper as you answer the questions. Take the thoughts out of your head and the feelings from your heart, and put them down on paper. This helps you understand yourself more clearly. Self-awareness is part of the foundation for gaining *The Inside Advantage*. Use common sense to answer questions that are applicable for your needs.

You'll see that the first item says, "One thing I want to change is: _____." Think of something you would like to change. Before you write anything down, listen to the words you use and think about your intent. Are you focusing on what you want or what you don't want? If you thought, for example, "not to feel so self-conscious when making a presentation," it would be better to write: "to feel confident when making a presentation." If you want to eliminate a behavior such as biting your fingernails, focus on what you want—having nice-looking nails (not to stop biting them). You always want to focus on what you want as opposed to what you don't want. Think about yourself moving toward something positive rather than away from something negative. Do the same when you focus on your future vision.

Make sure you are clear when distinguishing the things over which you have control. If this is a change you hope will occur, but is not in your direct control, you may want to reconsider using your time and energy more wisely. Concentrate on matters within your power to change. Also, be open to the possibility that you might be able to change something that you have previously considered unchangeable or not in your control.

My guess is that many of you will answer "No" or "Not Sure" to the question: "Do I believe I can make this change?" Typically what holds us back lies in not believing deep down that we actually can do it. Begin to trust in yourself, because you can change. You can develop the beliefs that you need. You can accomplish extraordinary things!

I invite you to share your extraordinary accomplishments by writing to me in care of:

> Request, Inc.
> P.O. Box 21269
> Little Rock, AR 72221-1269

# Extraordinary Changes
# Questionnaire™

You may want to write your responses to these questions on a sheet of paper, focusing on one specific change at a time. Answer what is applicable to you and your situation.

## A. Desire and Motivation

1. One thing I would like to change is

   _____.

2. Is this in my control?        Yes        No        Not Sure

3. Why is it important that I accomplish this? (Get to the heart of it.) The reason I want to do this is because

   _____.

4. Do I believe I can make this change?    Yes        No        Not Sure (Almost anything is possible if you believe in yourself.)

5. Am I ready and willing to make this change?

   Yes        No        Not Sure

   If you:
   (1) have decided what you want to change,
   (2) know that it is in your direct control,
   (3) have been inspired and motivated,
   (4) believe you can do it, and
   (5) feel you are ready, then
   (6) commit yourself to using your time and energy to accomplish something extraordinary.
   Expect it to happen!

## B. Examine where you are now. (Present)

In general, what is going on in your life right now? How do you think of yourself? Are you the kind of person you want to be? What is important to you (values)? Do you have a sense of purpose? If so, what is it? Are you accomplishing what you want? Now focus more specifically:

1. Does what you want to change have to do with the  way you are *thinking*?

   Yes        No        Not Sure

   If you chose "Yes" or "Not Sure," think about the current thoughts you want to change. List the negative thoughts and statements that you make concerning this.

2. Does this have to do with the way you are *feeling*?

   Yes        No        Not Sure

   If you chose "Yes" or "Not Sure," think about the feelings (physical or emotional) you want to change. List the negative emotional feelings and/or the physical sensations you experience concerning this.

3. Does this change have to do with what you are *doing* or  how you are behaving?

   Yes        No        Not Sure

   If you chose "Yes" or "Not Sure," think about your current actions. Write down what are you doing now which causes you to be dissatisfied with this situation. (Be specific.)


**C. Take a look at where you have been.** (Past)

As you read the next three questions, think about and write down how your past plays a role in your current situation.

1. What do you think happened in the past that causes you to think, feel and/or behave the way you do now? Brainstorm here if you need to, and jot down any ideas that come to you. Typically these will be negative experiences. Remain focused on your specific objective.
2. Which negative emotions are you carrying with you? (See "Examining Negative Emotions" in Chapter 15.)

   What benefits do you gain from them? (This is a tough question. Think this through and you will gain insight.)

   Do you want or need to continue holding on to them?

   Yes        No        Not Sure

Can you give yourself permission to let go of what you no longer want or need?

Yes       No       Not Sure

3. Next, think about how you might have interpreted your experiences. How would you summarize your interpretation(s) about what happened to you? In other words, what did you learn from the past about yourself, your capabilities, or the world around you? Write the answers down and remember to remain focused on what you want to change.

**D. Imagine *where you want to go.*** (Future Vision)

How do you define personal success? Keep in mind not only the destination, but also the journey. Remember to focus on what you want, with the idea of moving toward something positive.

1. Ideally, how do you want to think? What specific thoughts, concepts, and beliefs do you need firmly established in your mind to enable you to accomplish what you want? Write down anything that you think would be helpful.

2. How do you want to feel? Describe the ideal feelings you want to experience (physical and/or emotional).

3. What do you want to do? Ideally, what do you want your specific action(s) to be?

4. When you accomplish this extraordinary task, how will your life be better? What benefits will you gain?

Use what you have learned about yourself and your experiences to help you live more joyfully and successfully in the future you envision. Put your mind to work; then let it work for you automatically! (See "Steps to Follow for Maximum Results" in Chapter 17.)

**Extraordinary things are within your reach!**

# Index

## A

Active visualization 71, 72
Adrenaline 27, 48, 86
Affirmations 28, 41
AIDS 160
Aloneness 126–127
Alpha waves 27, 28
Anchoring 67
Anger 115
Anxiety xvii, 47, 50, 94
Apple 54, 60, 123
Appreciation of life 148–150
Associative perspective awareness 73
Attention 30–32
Attitude xvi, 97, 99, 139
Aurelius, Marcus 2
Authenticity 151
Autonomic nervous system 80–84
  parasympathetic 80, 82
  sympathetic 80, 81

## B

Barasch, M.I. 106
Beliefs 11, 36–37, 39–43
  wellness 110
Belly breaths 78, 86, 93
Benson, Herbert 25, 104
Beta waves 26–27, 28, 31, 135
Blame 3, 15, 115
Borysenko, Joan 104
Bowling 143
Brain (see also Mind)
  cerebral cortex 55
  hemispheres 24–25
  wave activity 26–28, 31, 42
Breathing 48–49
  belly breaths 78, 86, 93
  stress reduction 93
Bubble blowing 99
Buddhism 77
Buzman, Tony 25

## C

Cancer 104, 106, 108, 110
Cerebral cortex 55
Change
  inspiration as impetus 10
  long-term 2–3
  resistance to 8–9

Chemotherapy 159–160
Chopra, Deepak 106, 151
Churchill, Winston 28
Classical conditioning 67
Cleveland Clinic Foundation 107
Cognitive dissonance 19
Colors 62, 63, 99
Comfort zone 4
Communicating feelings to others
  145–146
Concentration 140
Confrontation 81, 89
Conscious effort 33, 57
Control
  charting your course 21–22
  inner-directedness 3
  negative thoughts 126
  subconscious mind 23–24
Cooperation 25
Cortisol 85
Courage 5, 117
Covey, Stephen R. 59
Creativity 20, 50, 140

## D

da Vinci, Leonardo 25, 55
Daydreams 10, 24, 27, 54, 60, 95
Death 71, 81, 93, 110, 111, 149
Decision-making 140
Deep breathing 48–49
Deep relaxation 50–51
Delta waves 27
Descartes, René 137
Disease 85, 104, 106
Dissociation 89–92
Dissociative perspective awareness 73
Drucker, Peter 10
Drugs 9, 105

## E

Earrings 13
EEG 26
Eliot, T.S. xviii
*Eight Weeks to Optimum Health* (Weil)
  105
Einstein, A. 25, 59, 77
Electroencephalograph 26
Emerson, Ralph Waldo 39